# COMPUTER TOOLS

## FOR THE ENGINEER & SCIENTIST

RICHARD CAMPBELL

A WORKBOOK FOR PROBLEM SOLVING AND PROGRAMMING IN MATLAB®, Mathcad®, and the TI-89®

Kendall Hunt
publishing company

Cover image © Shutterstock, Inc.

Kendall Hunt
publishing company

www.kendallhunt.com
*Send all inquiries to:*
4050 Westmark Drive
Dubuque, IA 52004-1840



ISBN 978-1-4652-1229-0



Printed in the United States of America
10 9 8 7 6 5 4 3 2 1

# Contents

# Introduction

The programmable digital computer has revolutionized technology. It provides the engineer and scientist with powerful tools to solve problems and create solutions that our forefathers could only theorize. A twenty-first century engineering and science education must now require that the student be conversant in computer operations, algorithm development, and usage of the many general applications developed for these disciplines.

Unlike computer scientists and software engineers, however, the working engineer or scientist rarely writes complex applications or extensive computer code. For many disciplines, learning a specific computer language is unnecessary. Rather, an engineer in industry will more likely use programmable applications to create solutions for unique or specialized designs. The basics of computer programming, primarily algorithm development and translating a mathematical solution to code, transcends a specific language. The engineer must be conversant in a variety of tools in order to select the best tool for the task at hand.

Many engineering curriculae are now introducing these skills to the freshman engineering student. Students gain knowledge of the tools and their capabilities, but not the engineering theory that is behind the analysis. However, they are prepared to take these skills to the next level and apply them in their subsequent engineering coursework.

There are several excellent texts available for teaching freshmen the various tools used in the classroom and in industry. This workbook does not intend to duplicate those texts, instead provides a supplement to them. Classroom experience has shown that the best way to reinforce this learning is . . . to do. And do over and over, with a wide variety of problems in various engineering disciplines. This workbook is designed for such reinforcement. Many different types of problems are presented, along with repetitive exercises, to allow the student to gain confidence in the methods learned. Problems from disciplines such as electrical, mechanical, thermodynamics, and aerospace are provided to show the broad range of application of these tools and different solution approaches. One constant remains throughout. That constant is the emphasis on a problem solving methodology or solution process that can be applied regardless of the type of problem.

Two of the most common computer tools used in industry are MATLAB and Mathcad. Both have unique user interfaces and very different ways of doing the same thing. MATLAB is an ideal tool for teaching programming and creating solutions to solve specialized problems. Mathcad, with its graphical user interface (GUI), is particularly well suited to solving mathematical equations and preparing written reports that must contain extensive analysis; both have their place in industry.

The use of the TI-89 handheld calculator is also included. This calculator enjoys the widespread use because of the mathematical capabilities, including matrix algebra, and the ability to be programmed with structured programming techniques. Because of its portability, user-defined functions and programs are easily accessible in the classroom and lab.

This workbook assumes that the reader already has mathematical and programming skills to do the exercises. A common theme is to present the same problem in different formats to learn how each of the three tools is used for the same solution. As the user will find, each tool has its plus and minus when it comes to solving different kinds of problems or creating a specified output. It is believed that this will help the user to appreciate not only the advantage of a common problem solving methodology regardless of the tool but also to determine the best tool for the particular requirement.

CHAPTER 1

# TI-89

## 1.1 TI-89® BASICS

The TI-89® calculator is the standard calculator for many engineering students. The TI-89 is a powerful computing tool, which not only performs all manner of mathematical operations but can be programmed with user-defined functions and applications. This section will help students get started, point to reference resources, and show some shortcuts and tricks to help learn to use it easily.

The current model available is the TI-89 Titanium, and this chapter will refer only to that model. However, earlier versions operate in a manner similar to TI-89 Titanium. The manual that comes with the TI-89 is called a "guidebook" by Texas Instruments® (TI), as it does not contain detailed programming and operating information. A comprehensive set of electronic information is available on CD-ROM (which may have been received with the product), and also online at *education.ti.com/guides*. It is recommended that the new user read through at least page 17 of the TI-89 guidebook to get started, and download the complete operating manual for future reference.

Throughout this chapter, reference is made to certain user preferences and operating methods. The objective of these methods is to minimize keystrokes whenever possible. This philosophy applies to most operations described in this book. These methods are by no means directive, and students are encouraged to use the methods that are most comfortable for them. Also, this section is not intended to be comprehensive, but it will highlight methods discovered, which make the TI-89 easy to use.

### 1.1.1 Look at the Keyboard and Become Familiar with the Names and layout of the Keys (Figure 1.1.1)

Turn **ON** the TI-89 and observe the Application Desktop displaying the icons of the built-in Apps.

Note:

- **F1** Menu has a function to set the clock
- the bottom Status Line (Figure 1.1.2) shows settings information
    - MAIN indicates the current folder where data and programs will be stored. The user may define other folders to organize data and programs.

**Figure 1.1.1**

- "a" in a black box (the Alpha Lock symbol) indicates that the keyboard is in the "alphabetic" mode, which means the number or function on a key is ignored and only the letter is typed. Jump to an Application on the Desktop by just typing the first letter when in Alpha Lock mode.
- RAD (or DEG) indicates the angle mode for calculations, RADians (or DEGrees).
- AUTO indicates the Exact/Approx Mode (more on this later).

Figure 1.1.2

## 1.1.2 HOME Key

It returns to the primary calculation and display screen.

a. Keyboard modifier keys (Figure 1.1.3): **2ND** (blue), Diamond ♦ (yellow), ↑ (grey up arrow—the "shift" key), **ALPHA** (white) keys allow you to select different functions and operations on the same key. Note that most of the other keys have blue, yellow, and white options corresponding to these modifiers.

Figure 1.1.3

Alphabetic operations: Select **ALPHA** once to enter a letter. Select **ALPHA** twice (or **2ND ALPHA**) to invoke the "Alpha Lock" mode, every keystroke will enter text until **ALPHA** is selected again to Unlock.

b. - **ESC**—use this to cancel an operation or get back to the previous screen.
   - **APPS**—returns to the Apps Desktop
   - Arrow Keys—for scrolling L/R, Up/Down. "page-scroll" by holding down the **2ND** key.

c. Tabs **F1–F5** (at the top): Select a Tab key to view handy menu operations. To select a command, scroll down and hit Enter or just type the number of the command. Scroll the Tabs left and right with the arrow keys. Check out:

   **F1** Tools—**8**:Clear Home

   **F6** Clean Up—**1**:Clear a-z; this is important when storing values as variables (more later).

d. Select **2ND CUSTOM** (above the **HOME** key) and see that new Tabs have appeared with more commands in the Menu. This is the built-in Custom Menu (See Example 1.2.3-4 on how to create a user-defined custom menu). Check out:

   **F4** Units—For example, on the command line enter "4.5", then **F4** and select **_ft**. Hit **ENTER** and see 1.372_m. The default mode for the calculator is in the Units SI mode, so all units will be converted to SI. Refer to the user manual for more information on units conversion.

## 1.1.3 MODE Key

Display Digits—Fix versus Float. Try this: select FLOAT 4 and calculate 365/.27=, and 365/44.27= and note the format of the results. Now change to FIX 4 and perform the same calculations and compare the results. For engineering calculations, FIX 4 is good for general use, then round-off for significant figures when presenting results. Of course, the user should select the display they prefer.

Angle—select the angle mode Radians or Degrees. Beginning engineering students may be uncomfortable using Radian mode, but it is necessary to be familiar with it. Some functions, such as for complex numbers, do not work in Degree mode.
Pretty Print—turn this ON. It makes equations and matrices easier to read.
Exact/Approx.—This determines the way the results of numerical calculations are displayed. (more later).
Unit System—changes from SI to US/English and back.

## 1.1.4 CATALOG Key

This selects the CATALOG, which lists every command and operator in the TI-89. It starts with Symbols and lists every command alphabetically. Jump to anywhere in the list by simply hitting the letter key for the command needed. Alpha Mode does not have to be selected. For example, to jump to the Absolute Value function "abs(" which is not on the keyboard, select **CATALOG**, then press "=" (for A) and the catalog list will jump to the A's. Use the Arrow (up or down) key to go to the desired command and press Enter, and the command will be placed in the Home command line. There is also a catalog called **MATH (2ND 5)**, which lists only the math-related functions in the **CATALOG**.

NOTE: All functions that are listed in the preceding text include the left parenthesis, such as "abs(", saving a keystroke.

## 1.1.5 Exact/Approx

A binary digital computer cannot normally represent a decimal number, or the result of a calculation, to an exact accurate decimal place. For example, one-third is either 1/3 (exactly) or 0.33333 (approximately). One can choose how numerical results should be displayed using the Exact/Approx mode. Do this: Set **MODE** to Exact. Calculate 4/7, 4/7.0, $\sqrt{33}$ $\sqrt{33.0}$ and note the displayed results (square root operator is **2ND ×**). Now set **MODE** to Approx and do the same calculations. Now set **MODE** to Auto and do the same calculations. Auto Mode is generally more convenient. If a decimal answer is desired, include a decimal point in one of the operands, or use the **♦-ENTER**, which forces an approximate result.

Here is an interesting result: Set **MODE** Auto and calculate 1/3*3-1=, then calculate 1/3.*3-1= (note the added decimal point). Why are the results different? Are they really different?

## 1.1.6 Math Operations

The calculator uses "algebraic hierarchy", which defines the order in which math operations will be performed; i.e., negation (–), exponents, multiply/divide, add/subtract.

Potential Gotcha: Note the key below the **3** key (Figure 1.1.4), it is a **(–)**. This is the negation key, not the subtraction operator (it is also the **SPACE** key in Alpha mode). Use the negation key to enter a negative number, as strange results are displayed sometimes.

The math operators are the keys on the right-hand side of the keyboard. From top to bottom they are: ^ (exponent), ÷ (divide), × (multiply), – (subtraction), + (addition). Also conveniently provided is the equal sign =, and the parentheses () and the comma, along with the most commonly used variables **x**, **y**, **z**, and **t**. These keys are used frequently for entering expressions; hence, they are made available without the need for modifier keys, thus saving keystrokes.

**Figure 1.1.4**

Note that using the parentheses **()** properly will change the order of calculation as the operation inside the **()** will be performed first regardless of the hierarchy. For example:

Calculate 3+4*5, **ENTER**; calculate (3+4)*5, **Enter**; then note the results. Or do the second equation this way: press 3+4, **Enter**, × 5, **Enter** (in that exact sequence). Notice that when the × was pressed, that **ans(1)*** appeared in the command line, where **ans(1)** is the result of the previous operation. This allows long strings of calculations to be made without having to enter everything all at once. Also, intermediate calculations can be reviewed.

### 1.1.7 Storing Values as Variables

Do this: **F6** Clean Up, select **1:** Clear a-z. This clears the memory of any previously stored values in the single letter variables. Now on the command line, enter **ALPHA a**. The display should just show "a", because no value has been assigned to "a". Now type **3 STO> (ALPHA) a**. The result, 3, appears in the display. To verify that **a** now has the value of 3, type **a** on the command line and hit **ENTER**. Calculate **a+4=**. Calculate **A+4=** (use the **ALPHA-SHIFT** to get the capital **A**) and note that *variable names are not case sensitive*. **a** will continue to hold the value 3 until a different value is **STO**red, until deleted, or "Clear a-z" is executed. Why is this important? If a value is stored in a variable name, and that variable is later used in a calculation, it will use the stored value, giving possibly undesired results, as when doing symbolic operations (such as indefinite integrals, for example). Since **x**, **y**, **z**, **t** and other single letter variables are used so often, the "Clear a-z" is a convenient way to reset all variables before beginning a new problem. As good operating practice, always "Clear a-z" before beginning a new problem or programming exercise.

HINT: Select **2ND VAR-LINK** (the Subtraction key). This gives a listing of all the variables, functions, and programs that have been created and stored in memory. The Tabs give commands (such as DELETE and RENAME) to manage these items.

This is just the tip of the iceberg of a very complex computing device. It will benefit the user to become familiar with the Guidebook and the online material available.

## 1.2 TI-89 WORKED EXAMPLES

### 1.2.1 Matrices and Matrix Algebra on the TI-89

The TI-89 calculator is well suited for performing matrix math. Matrices of any order (and row and column vectors) may be entered by one of two methods: directly on the command line or with the Data/Matrix Editor. Command line entry is suitable for small vectors and matrices. The Data/Matrix Editor simplifies the entry and editing of large matrices.

#### Example 1.2.1-1 Creating a vector on the command line.

Create the row vector **a** = [2 3 4] by entering

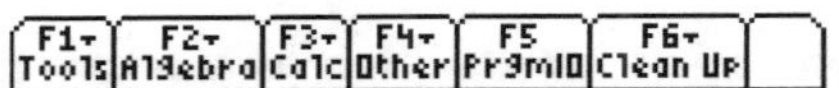


```
■[2  3  4] → a            [2  3  4]
[2,3,4]→a
MAIN          RAD AUTO      FUNC      1/30
```

Create the column vector $\mathbf{b} = \begin{bmatrix} 5 \\ 3 \\ 1 \end{bmatrix}$ by entering

F1 Tools | F2 Algebra | F3 Calc | F4 Other | F5 PrgmIO | F6 Clean Up

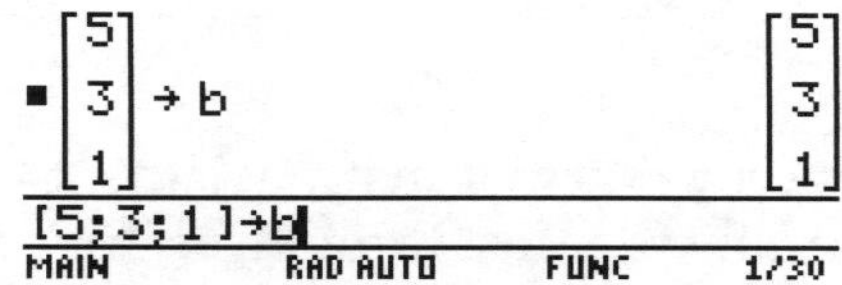


The comma delimiter is required for entering row elements, and the semicolon delimiter establishes the next row. Note that the semicolon is 2ND-9, the left bracket is 2ND-comma, and the right bracket is 2ND-divide.

Create the 2x3 matrix $\mathbf{c} = \begin{bmatrix} 1 & 2 & 3 \\ 4 & 5 & 6 \end{bmatrix}$ by entering

[1,2,3;4,5,6]→c

MAIN RAD AUTO FUNC 1/30

## Example 1.2.1-2 Using the Data/Matrix Editor

Select the Data/Matrix Editor from the Apps screen

**1**: selects the last matrix edited.

**2**: chooses an existing matrix from the user folder.

**3**: starts the creation of a new matrix variable.

MAIN RAD AUTO FUNC

To create new matrix variable, select **3:New**, then Type >2:Matrix:

Enter the variable name, and matrix dimensions:

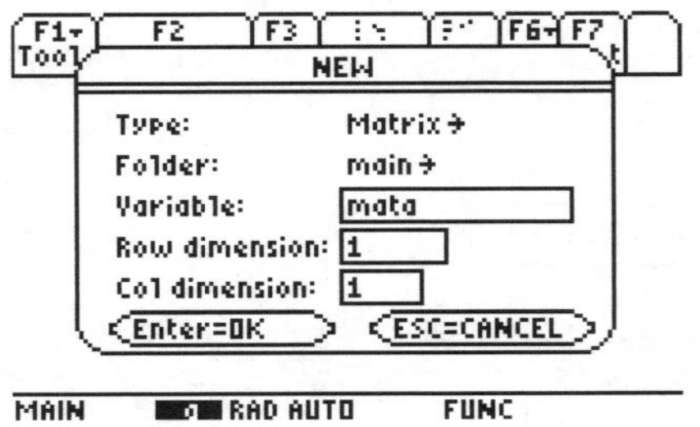


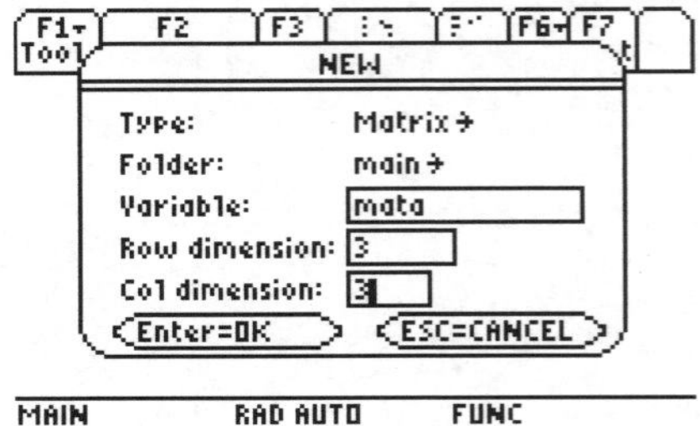


An array or table is presented for easy entry of matrix elements. Enter the element value and hit Enter, the entry point will automatically progress through each element position in row order. Errors can easily be corrected by arrowing back to the correct element.

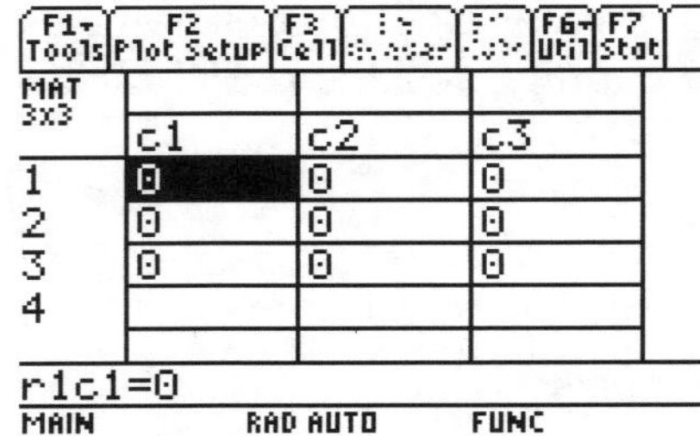


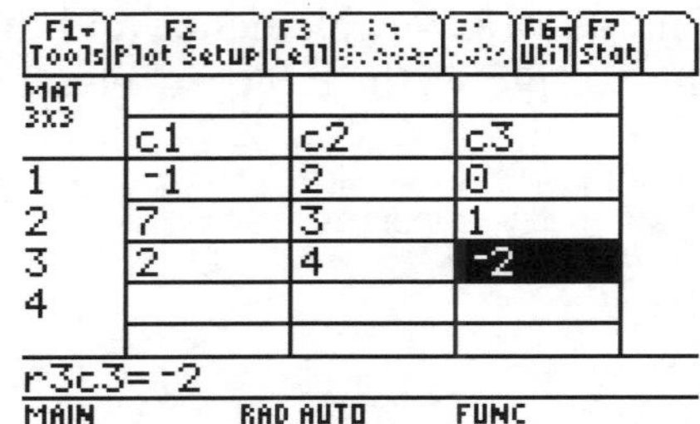


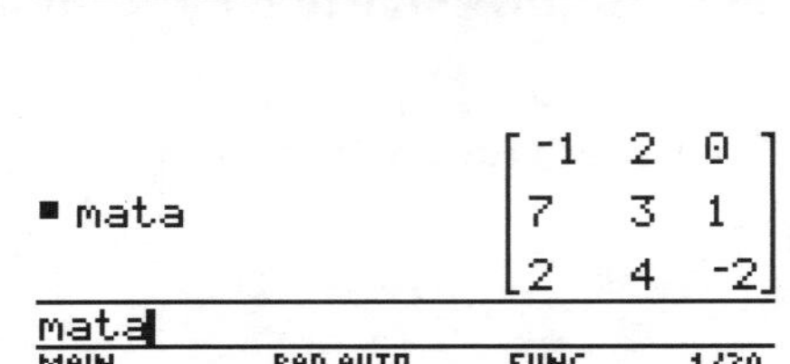


## Example 1.2.1-3 Matrix math

Using the previously created matrices **a**, **b**, and **mata**:

a. Multiply **a*b**

b. Multiply **b*a**

c. Multiply **a*mata**

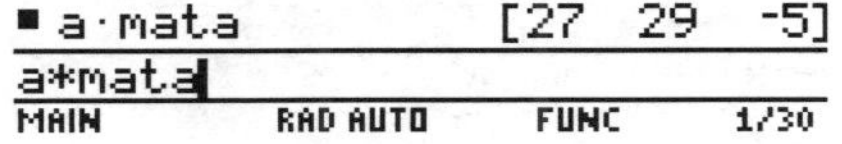

d. Multiply **mata*b** (Note that **b*mata** results in an error)

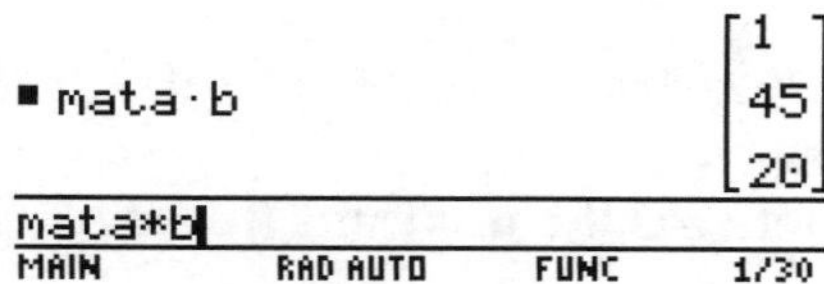


e. Add **a+b**$^{\mathbf{T}}$

```
■ a + b^T                 [7  6  5]
a+bT
MAIN      RAD AUTO    FUNC    1/30
```

f. Find the determinant of **mata**

```
■ det(mata)                    42
det(mata)
MAIN      RAD AUTO    FUNC    1/30
```

g. Find the inverse of **mata**

```
F1 Tools | F2 Algebra | F3 Calc | F4 Other | F5 PrgmIO | F6 Clean Up

■ mata^-1
        [ -5/21   2/21   1/21  ]
        [ 8/21    1/21   1/42  ]
        [ 11/21   4/21  -17/42 ]
mata^-1
MAIN      RAD AUTO    FUNC    1/30
```

And using ♦-Enter

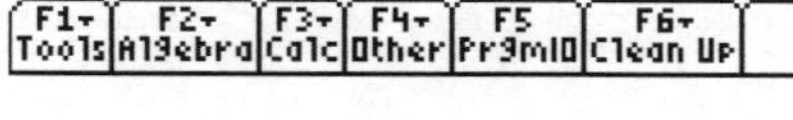


```
■ mata^-1
        [ -.2381   .0952   .0476 ]
        [ .3810    .0476   .0238 ]
        [ .5238    .1905  -.4048 ]
mata^-1
MAIN      RAD AUTO    FUNC    1/30
```

## 1.2.2 Complex Numbers on the TI-89

The TI-89 is particularly handy at dealing with complex numbers. Three forms of the same complex number are defined in mathematics; the rectangular (or standard) form, the exponential form, and the polar form (see Figure 1.2.1)

a. Rectangular Form: $z = a + bi$, where $a$ is the real part Re($z$), and $b$ is the imaginary part Im($z$).
b. Exponential Form: $z = re^{\theta I}$, where $r$ is the modulus (magnitude) and θ is the argument (angle).
c. Polar Form: $z = r(\cos\theta + i\sin\theta)$, where $r$ is the modulus and $\theta$ is the argument. Note that since $a = r\cos\theta$ and $b = r\sin\theta$, the polar form is a combination of the rectangular and exponential forms. This comes from Euler's equation: $e^{\theta I} = \cos\theta + i\sin\theta$.

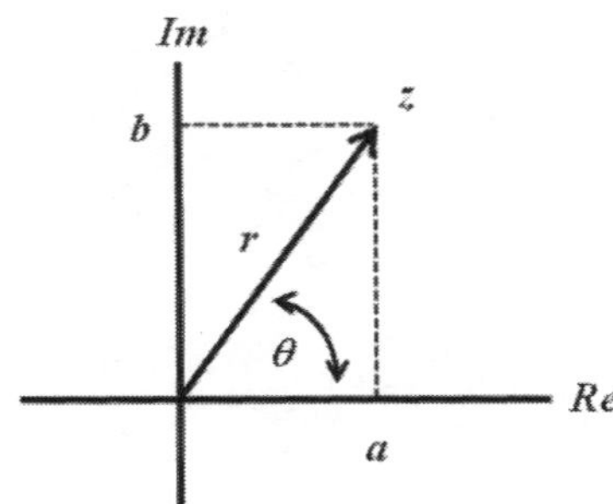


**Figure 1.2.1** Argand Diagram for complex numbers

The TI-89 has display formats for complex numbers. Navigate to **MODE**, **Page 1** and select "Complex Format". The **REAL** setting should not be used because this suppresses complex results. The **RECTANGULAR** setting displays complex numbers in the rectangular format. The **POLAR** setting displays complex numbers in an exponential format (do not confuse format definitions with display settings) (Figure 1.2.2).

**Figure 1.2.2** Complex Format Menu

The display format will differ depending on whether **MODE, Angle** is set to **DEGREE** or **RADIAN** mode. Some complex number functions will not work in **DEGREE** mode, so it is always best to select **RADIAN** mode when working with complex numbers.

Note that the imaginary number $\boldsymbol{i}$ ($\sqrt{-1}$) is above the **CATALOG** key (not alpha $i$).

## Example 1.2.2-1

Given $zz = 1.9\,e^{(3.5-0.3i)} + (2-5i)$, Find:

a. $zz$ in Rectangular (Standard) Form

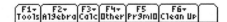

```
F1▾   F2▾     F3▾  F4▾   F5     F6▾
Tools Algebra Calc Other PrgmIO Clean Up

■ 1.9·e^(3.5 - .3·i) + 2 - 5·i
              62.1092 - 23.5939·i
1.9e^(3.5-0.3i)+(2-5i)
MAIN        RAD AUTO      FUNC      1/30
```

b. *zz* in Exponential Form

```
F1▾   F2▾     F3▾  F4▾   F5     F6▾
Tools Algebra Calc Other PrgmIO Clean Up

■ 1.9·e^(3.5 - .3·i) + 2 - 5·i
                    e^(-.3630·i)·66.4396
1.9e^(3.5-0.3i)+(2-5i)
MAIN        RAD AUTO     FUNC       1/30
```

c. *zz* in Polar Form $zz = 66.44[\cos(-0.363) + i\sin(-0.363)]$

d. argument (angle), arg(*zz*)

```
F1▾    F2▾
Matrix Complex

■ zz                e^(-.3630·i)·66.4396
■ angle(zz)                      -.3630
angle(zz)
MAIN        RAD AUTO     FUNC       2/30
```

e. Re(*zz*)

```
F1▾    F2▾
Matrix Complex

■ zz                e^(-.3630·i)·66.4396
■ real(zz)                      62.1092
real(zz)
MAIN        RAD AUTO     FUNC       2/30
```

f. Im(*zz*)

```
F1▾    F2▾
Matrix Complex

■ zz                e^(-.3630·i)·66.4396
■ imag(zz)                     -23.5939
imag(zz)
MAIN        RAD AUTO     FUNC       2/30
```

g. mod(*zz*) (absolute value function recognizes a complex argument)

```
F1▾    F2▾
Matrix Complex

■ zz                e^(-.3630·i)·66.4396
■ |zz|                          66.4396
abs(zz)
MAIN        RAD AUTO     FUNC       2/30
```

h. conj(*zz*)

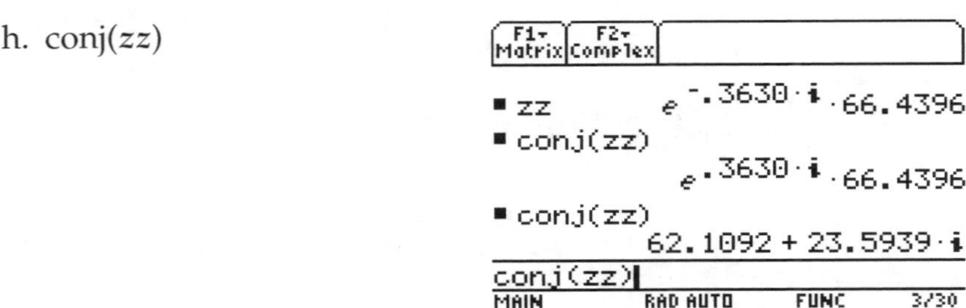


## Example 1.2.2-2

Find all the roots of $z^4 - 4iz = 0$ using the TI-89 function ***csolve***, and express the results in rectangular form. When results are larger than that can fit on the Home screen, an arrow appears to prompt the user to scroll into the Home screen and scroll to the right to see all the results.

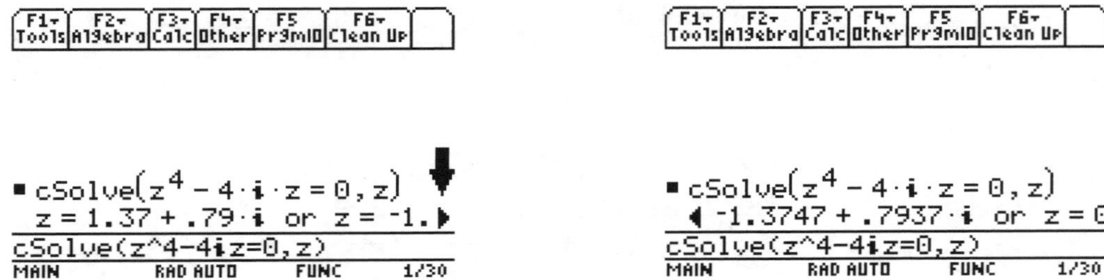


## 1.2.3 Programming the TI-89

These examples demonstrate how to use the Program Editor to key in a user-defined program, and several methods for creating Function Programs. The TI-89 recognizes two types of programs; application programs using the definition **Prgm . . . EndPrgm** (Figure 1.2.3), and function programs using the definition **Func . . . EndFunc** (Figure 1.2.4),. Both types can use structured programming blocks similar to those found in C or MATLAB. Both types of programs can be added to the User's Catalog, and can be managed from the **2ND-VAR-LINK** key.

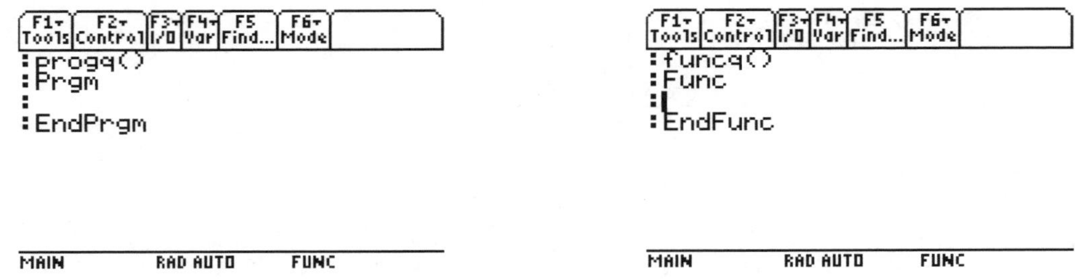


## Example 1.2.3-1

Create a program to display the first 10 numbers of the Fibonacci Series:

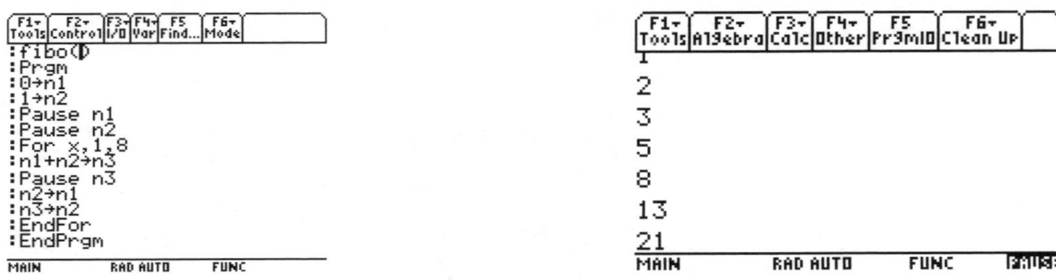

## Example 1.2.3-2

Create a function program to find the volume of a sphere for any radius, where Vol $= \frac{4}{3}\pi r^3$.

There are three ways to enter a function program in the TI-89:

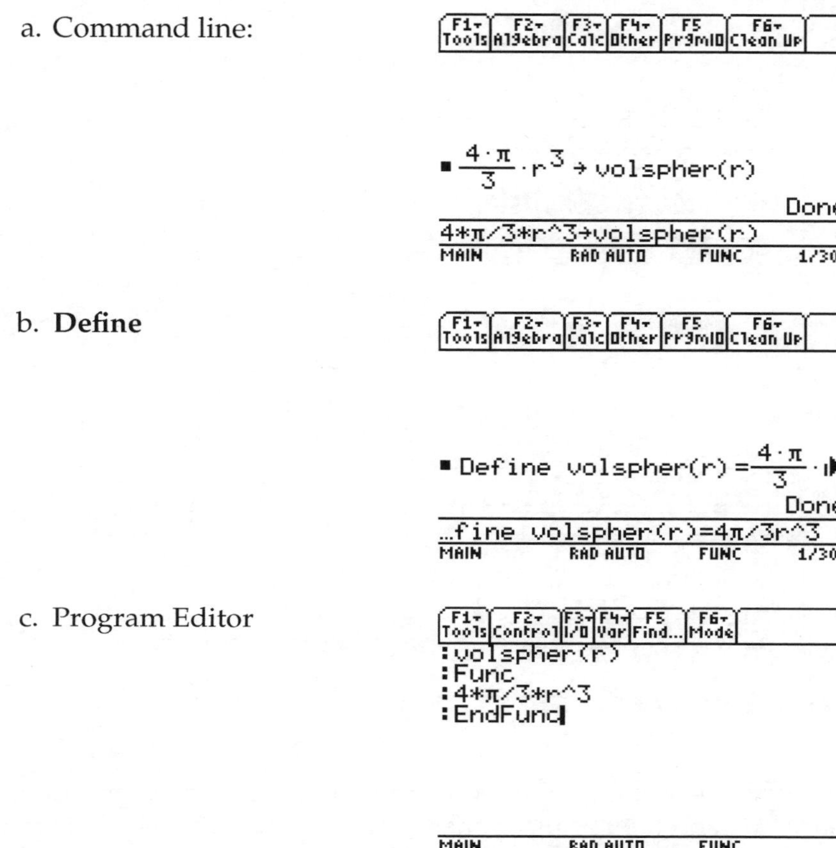


Note that the command line option can only be used for single equation–type functions. The **Define** command method can be used for multiline commands separated by a (:); however, this is a clumsy method since the command line viewing space is limited. A more complex function program (such as decision-making or looping) will require the Program Editor. Regardless of how the function program is initially created, it will be included in the User's Catalog (VAR-LINK), and can be edited from the Program Editor.

## Example 1.2.3-3

Use the Program Editor to create a function program that solves the ***signum*** function.

a. Select the Program Editor from the **APPS** menu

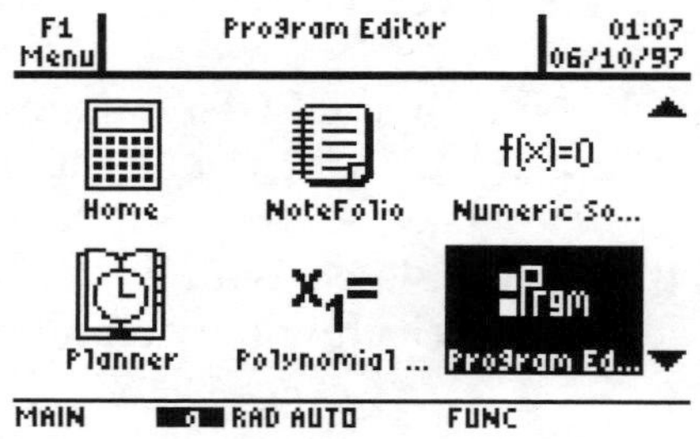

b. Select **3:New**

c. Select **2:Function**

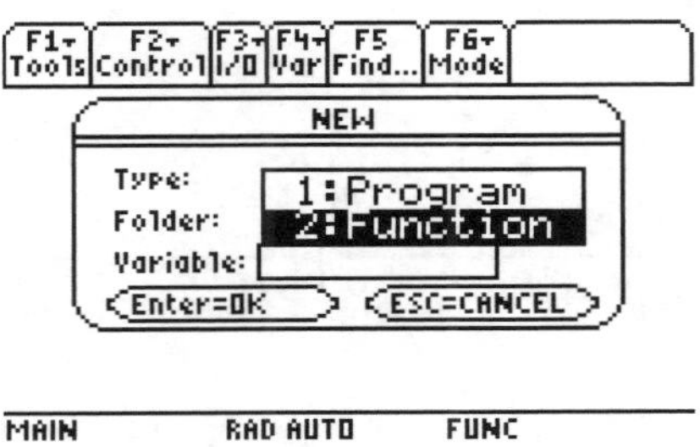


d. Enter the function name—*signum* (alpha is automatically turned on)

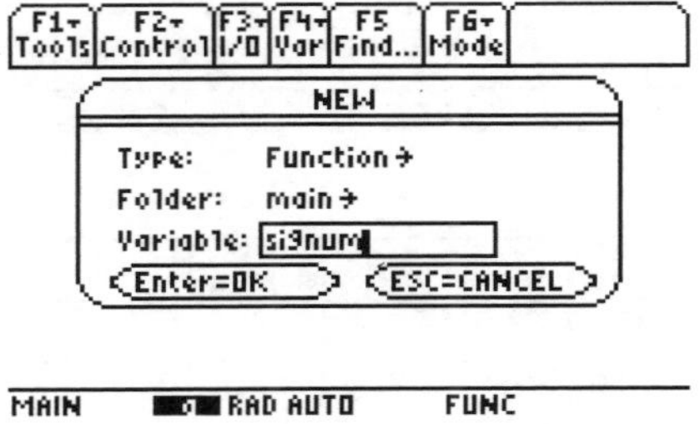


e. Enter the program from the keyboard or select the commands from the Catalog. This program demonstrates the **If . . . EndIf** structure and the **Local** command. Any variable that is not in the argument list must first be defined by the **Local** command. All variables are local variables to the function program only. Note that the **Return** command is optional if only the last computed value is to be returned.

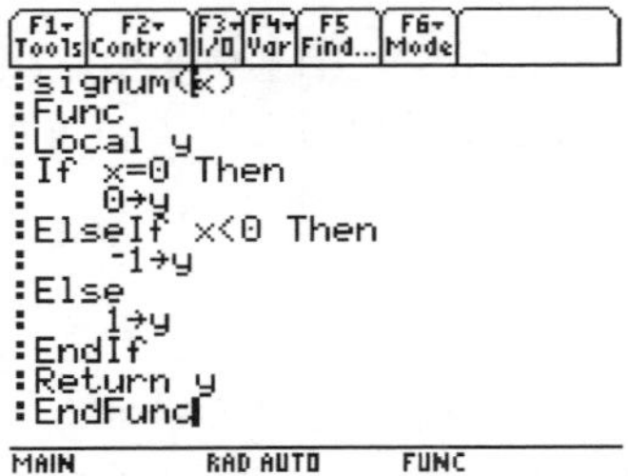


## Example 1.2.3-4 Creating a user-defined custom menu

The TI-89 has two built-in Menus selectable by the **F1-F5** function keys at the top of the keyboard. The menus are toggled by using the **2ND-CUSTOM** key (above the **HOME** key). The default menu (**F1-Tools**) cannot be changed. However, the built-in "custom" menu may be changed by creating a custom menu program that is completely defined by the user. The format and syntax of the built-in custom menu can be viewed by selecting the default menu **F6-Clean Up**, and selecting **3:Restore custom default**.

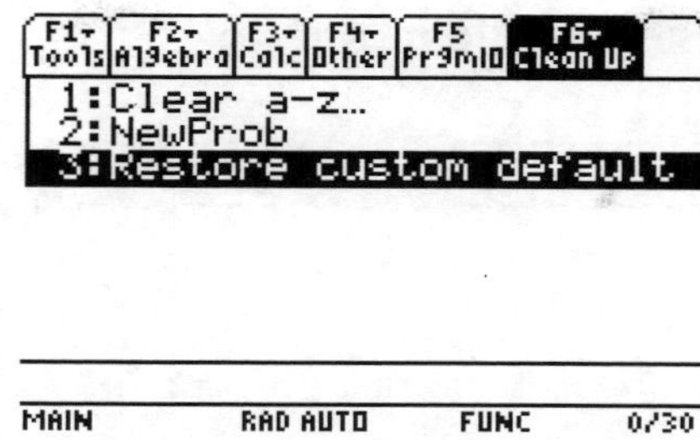


This action will place the entire command list into the command line, and hitting Enter will execute this program and create the built-in custom menu in memory. The code listing can also be found in the TI-89 User Guide. See the shortcut* hint below.

To create a user-defined custom menu program, start a new "Program" in the Program Editor and use the command block **Custom . . . EndCustm**. This tells the TI-89 to use the code that follows for the Menu Tab titles and command listings when the user selects CUSTOM from the keyboard. This new custom menu remains active on the function keys until the built-in custom default is restored, or a new custom menu program is executed.

a. Create a user-defined custom menu called ***user1*** that has menu tabs for matrix operations and complex number functions.

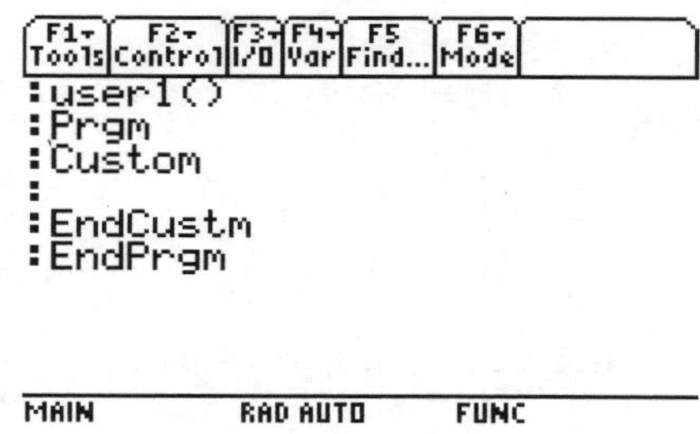


b. The "Title" command text will appear on the tab name on the Home screen. The "Item" command text can be any valid TI-89 command, executable program, or function. Note the inclusion of the left parenthesis to save a keystroke.

```
F1▾   F2▾     F3▾ F4▾ F5      F6▾
Tools Control I/O Var Find... Mode
:user1()
:Prgm
:Custom
:Title "Matrix"
:Item "det("
:Item "ref("
:Item "rref("
:Item "^-1"
:Item "norm("
:Title "Complex"
:Item "abs("
:Item "angle("
:Item "conj("
:Item "cSolve("
:Item "imag("
:Item "real("
:EndCustm
:EndPrgm
MAIN          RAD AUTO      FUNC
```

c. How the custom menu appears on the Home screen:

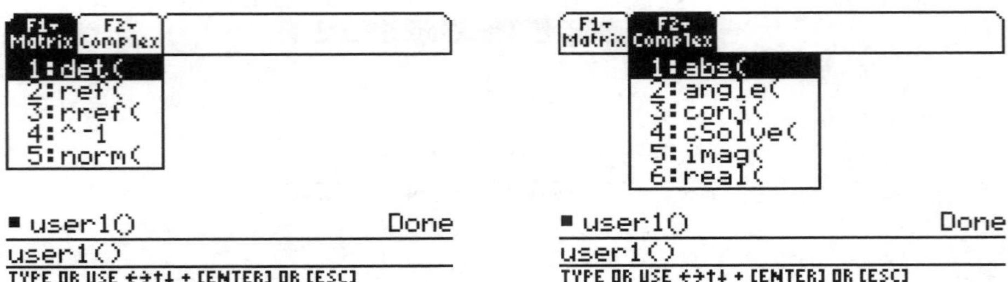


*Shortcut: After selecting **3:Restore custom default**, and after the program commands appear highlighted in the command line, select **COPY**. This will put the entire built-in custom menu program on the clipboard. Now simply create a **NEW** user-defined program and **PASTE** the clipboard program into the Program Editor. The user now has an editable custom menu program, instead of having to create one from scratch.

## 1.2.4 Solving Systems of Linear Equations on the TI-89

Many types of physical systems are represented by a system of linear equations. When the number of independent equations equals the number of unknowns, a unique solution may be found.

### Example 1.2.4-1

Solve the following system of equations for $[x,y,z]$.

$$\begin{aligned} x-2y+3z&=2\\ 2x+y-7z&=6\\ x-y-z&=1 \end{aligned}$$

convert to matrix form

$$\begin{bmatrix} 1 & -2 & 3\\ 2 & 1 & -7\\ 1 & -1 & -1 \end{bmatrix}\begin{bmatrix} x\\ y\\ z \end{bmatrix}=\begin{bmatrix} 2\\ 6\\ 1 \end{bmatrix}$$

The solution is $\begin{bmatrix} x\\ y\\ z \end{bmatrix}=A^{-1}*\bar{d}$

giving

$$\begin{aligned} x&=5\\ y&=3\\ z&=1 \end{aligned}$$

F1 Tools | F2 Algebra | F3 Calc | F4 Other | F5 PrgmIO | F6 Clean Up

■ a $\begin{bmatrix} 1 & -2 & 3\\ 2 & 1 & -7\\ 1 & -1 & -1 \end{bmatrix}$

■ d $\begin{bmatrix} 2\\ 6\\ 1 \end{bmatrix}$

■ $a^{-1}\cdot d$ $\begin{bmatrix} 5\\ 3\\ 1 \end{bmatrix}$

a^-1*d

MAIN RAD AUTO FUNC 3/30

## Example 1.2.4-2

The electric circuit has three unknown current loops, and the circuit can be represented by three linear equations using Ohm's law.

$$R_1 i_1 + R_2(i_1 - i_2) + R_3(i_1 - i_3) - V_1 = 0$$
$$R_2(i_2 - i_1) + R_4 i_2 + R_6(i_2 - i_3) = 0$$
$$R_3(i_3 - i_1) + R_6(i_3 - i_2) + R_5 i_3 = 0$$

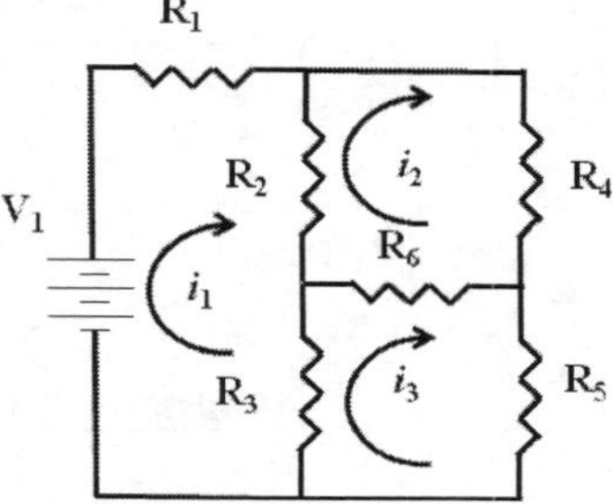


These equations must be rearranged and converted to $A * \overline{x} = \overline{d}$ form.

And collecting like terms

$$R_1 i_1 + R_2 i_1 + R_3 i_1 - R_2 i_2 - R_3 i_3 = V_1$$
$$-R_2 i_1 + R_2 i_2 + R_4 i_2 + R_6 i_2 - R_6 i_3 = 0$$
$$-R_3 i_1 - R_6 i_2 + R_3 i_3 + R_5 i_3 + R_6 i_3 = 0$$

can be arranged in the matrix equation

$$\begin{bmatrix} (R_1 + R_2 + R_3) & -R_2 & -R_3 \\ -R_2 & (R_2 + R_4 + R_6) & -R_6 \\ -R_3 & -R_6 & (R_3 + R_5 + R_6) \end{bmatrix} \begin{bmatrix} i_1 \\ i_2 \\ i_3 \end{bmatrix} = \begin{bmatrix} V_1 \\ 0 \\ 0 \end{bmatrix}$$

Solve for:

$$R_1 = 5\Omega \quad R_2 = 15\Omega \quad R_3 = 8\Omega \quad R_4 = 10\Omega \quad R_5 = 7\Omega \quad R_6 = 12\Omega \quad V_1 = 9V$$

$$\begin{bmatrix} 28 & -15 & -8 \\ -15 & 37 & -12 \\ -8 & -12 & 27 \end{bmatrix} \begin{bmatrix} i_1 \\ i_2 \\ i_3 \end{bmatrix} = \begin{bmatrix} 9 \\ 0 \\ 0 \end{bmatrix}$$

```
F1▾   F2▾     F3▾  F4▾   F5     F6▾
Tools Algebra Calc Other PrgmIO Clean Up

■ a^-1·d → i                    [.6099]
                                [.3574]
                                [.3395]
A^-1*d→i
MAIN        RAD AUTO      FUNC      1/30
```

## Example 1.2.4-3

Solving systems of linear equations by Gaussian elimination.

Certain systems with sparse matrices do not always produce reliable results when finding the inverse, so Gaussian elimination is used instead. This technique can produce either the Row Echelon Form or the Reduced Row Echelon Form, and the TI-89 has functions to calculate both [ **ref()** and **rref()** ]. Both require an "augmented matrix" as an argument, which is created by appending the **d** vector to the coefficient matrix $A$. Using the equations from Example 1.2.4-1, the augmented matrix would be

$$A_{aug} = \begin{bmatrix} 1 & -2 & 3 & 2 \\ 2 & 1 & -7 & 6 \\ 1 & -1 & -1 & 1 \end{bmatrix}$$

Create this augmented matrix using the Program Editor.

a. The Row Echelon Form solution is

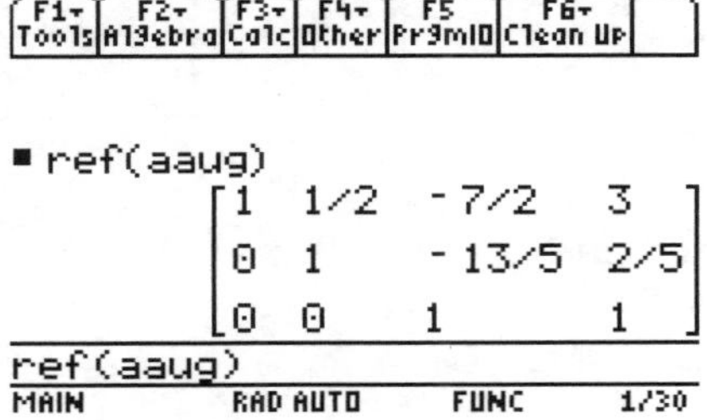


b. The Reduced Row Echelon Form solution is

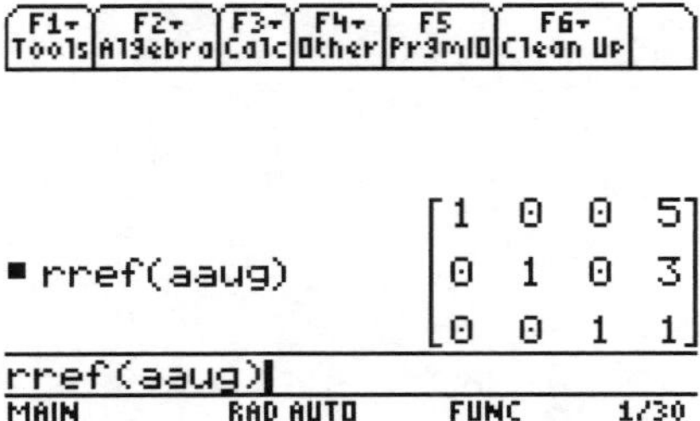


And the solution is read as

$$x = 5$$
$$y = 3$$
$$z = 1$$

CHAPTER 2

# MATLAB

## 2.1 MATLAB® BASICS

MATLAB®, an acronym meaning "Matrix Laboratory", can perform all manner of mathematical operations, and can be programmed with user-defined functions and applications using higher order language structured programming techniques. This section will help students get started, and show some shortcuts and tricks to help learn to use the tool easily. MATLAB is an excellent tool to learn how to program a computer, even without prior knowledge.

There are a variety of excellent texts available to learn MATLAB. An experienced engineer or a scientist who knows programming languages will find several advanced texts that present approaches to solving a variety of problems. There are also several texts suitable for the beginning freshman level college students studying engineering or science.

### 2.1.1 The MATLAB Environment

Upon starting MATLAB, the user is presented with the default four windows as shown in Figure 2.1.1. A discussion of the function of these windows will be left to the texts noted in the preceding text. Users may create a desktop to their liking by rearranging or resizing the windows, and by "undocking" any window, to freely move it about the desktop, using the hooked arrow in the upper right-hand corner of the window (Figure 2.1.2).

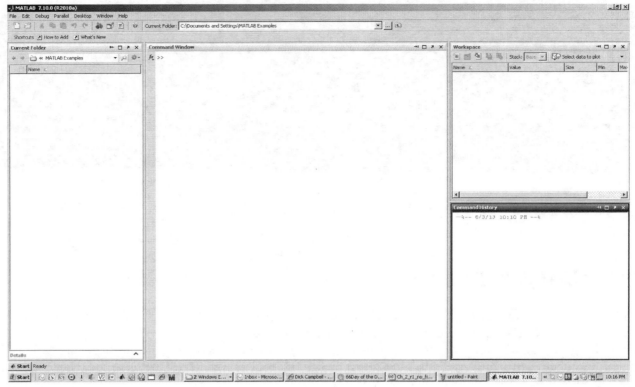

**Figure 2.1.1**

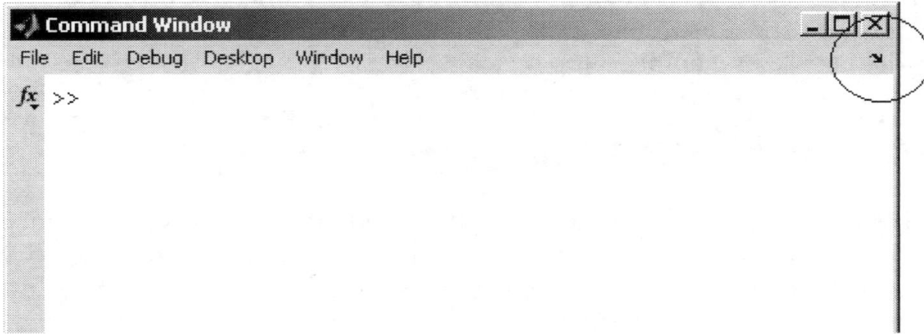


**Figure 2.1.2**

One other frequently used window is the Script or Function Editor to create user-defined program files. This window is discussed in Section 2.2.3, Programming in MATLAB.

There are other windows, such as interactive plot and import wizards. The uses of these special features are adequately discussed in any of the texts mentioned above. Examples are given in the following text to create plots and import data in Sections 2.2.5 and 2.2.6.

# 2.2 MATLAB WORKED EXAMPLES

## 2.2.1 Matrices and Matrix Algebra

By design, every variable created in MATLAB is a vector or more generally an array. By treating even scalars as vectors, many operations can be performed easily with built-in commands that obviate the requirement to write program code.

## Example 2.2.1-1

Creating a vector on the command Line.

The comma or space delimiter is required for entering row elements, and the semicolon delimiter establishes the next row.

a. Create the row vector $\mathbf{a} = \begin{bmatrix} 2 & 3 & 4 \end{bmatrix}$

b. Create the column vector

$$\mathbf{b} = \begin{bmatrix} 5 \\ 3 \\ 1 \end{bmatrix}$$

c. Create the 2x3 matrix

$$\mathbf{c} = \begin{bmatrix} 1 & 2 & 3 \\ 4 & 5 & 6 \end{bmatrix}$$

d. Create the 3x3 matrix

$$\mathbf{mata} = \begin{bmatrix} -1 & 2 & 0 \\ 7 & 3 & 1 \\ 2 & 4 & -2 \end{bmatrix}$$

The MATLAB session is

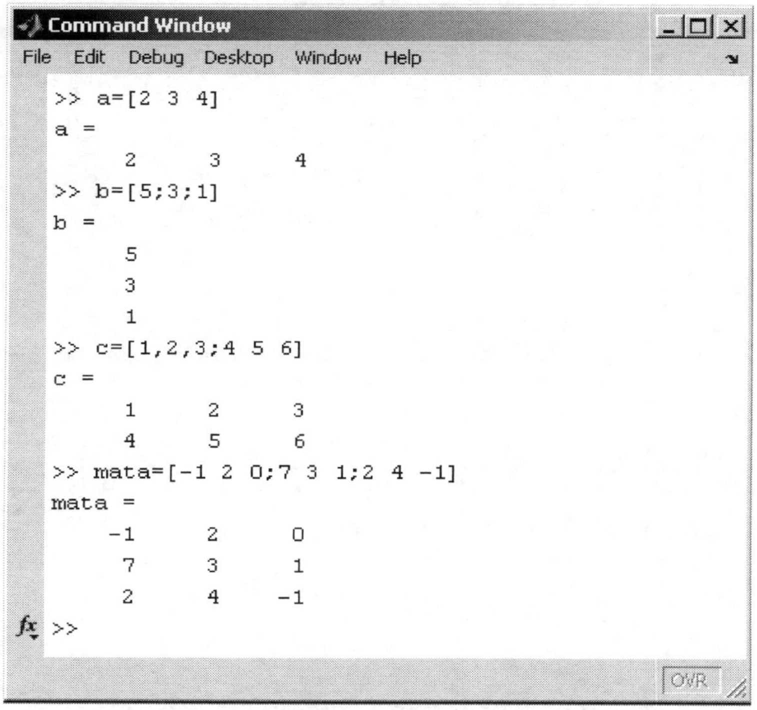

```
Command Window
File  Edit  Debug  Desktop  Window  Help

>> a=[2 3 4]
a =
      2     3     4
>> b=[5;3;1]
b =
      5
      3
      1
>> c=[1,2,3;4 5 6]
c =
      1     2     3
      4     5     6
>> mata=[-1 2 0;7 3 1;2 4 -1]
mata =
     -1     2     0
      7     3     1
      2     4    -1
fx >>
                                   OVR
```

## Example 2.2.1-2

Use the colon operator to create new matrices from *c*, and ***mata*** in Example 2.2.1-1:

a. Create $\mathbf{d}=\begin{bmatrix}-1 & 2 & 0\\ 7 & 3 & 1\\ 2 & 4 & -2\\ 4 & 5 & 6\end{bmatrix}$ from **mata** and row 2 of **c**.

b. Create $\mathbf{e}=\begin{bmatrix}2 & 4\\ 4 & 5\end{bmatrix}$ from **d**.

c. Create $\mathbf{f}=\begin{bmatrix}2 & 3\end{bmatrix}$ from **c**.

The MATLAB session is

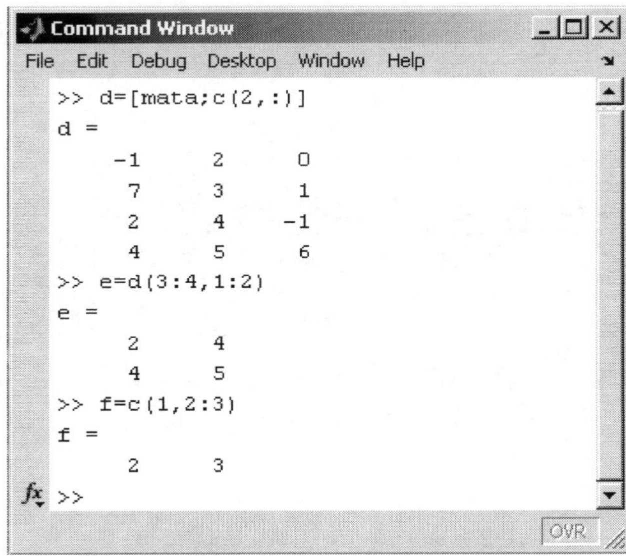


## Example 2.2.1-3 Matrix math.

Using the previously created matrices **a**, **b**, and **mata**:

a. Multiply **a*b**
b. Multiply **b*a**
c. Multiply **a*mata**
d. Multiply **mata*b** (Note that **b*mata** results in an error)
e. Add $\mathbf{a}+\mathbf{b}^{T}$
f. Find the determinant of **mata**
g. Find the inverse of **mata**

The MATLAB session is

```
Command Window
File Edit Debug Desktop Window Help
>> a*b
ans =
    23
>> b*a
ans =
    10    15    20
     6     9    12
     2     3     4
>> a*mata
ans =
    27    29    -5
>> mata*b
ans =
     1
    45
    20
>> b*mata
??? Error using ==> mtimes
Inner matrix dimensions must agree.

>> a+b'
ans =
     7     6     5
>> det(mata)
ans =
    42
>> mata^-1
ans =
   -0.2381    0.0952    0.0476
    0.3810    0.0476    0.0238
    0.5238    0.1905   -0.4048
>> inv(mata)
ans =
   -0.2381    0.0952    0.0476
    0.3810    0.0476    0.0238
    0.5238    0.1905   -0.4048
fx >>
```

## 2.2.2 Complex Numbers in MATLAB

The imaginary $\boldsymbol{i}, \boldsymbol{j} = \sqrt{-1}$ number is included in MATLAB's predefined variables. Complex numbers can be entered using these predefined variables without operators (Figure 2.2.1).

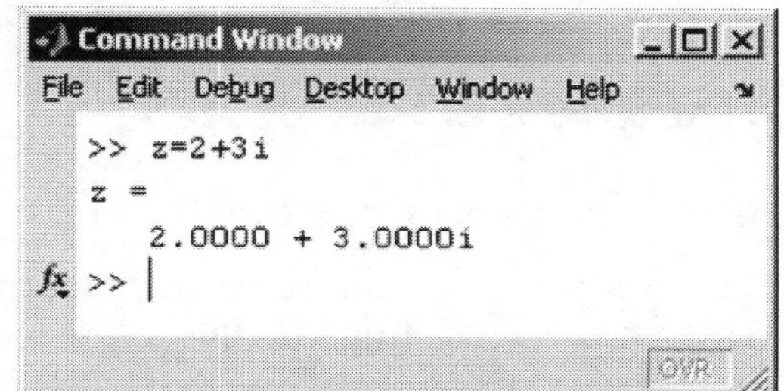


**Figure 2.2.1**

Note that MATLAB will only display one format (the rectangular format), but the standard complex number functions are available as demonstrated below. CAUTION:

It is possible to redefine the value of $i$ (or $j$) and produce unexpected results depending on how the equation is typed. Observe the different results in these two expressions for $z$ (Figure 2.2.2).

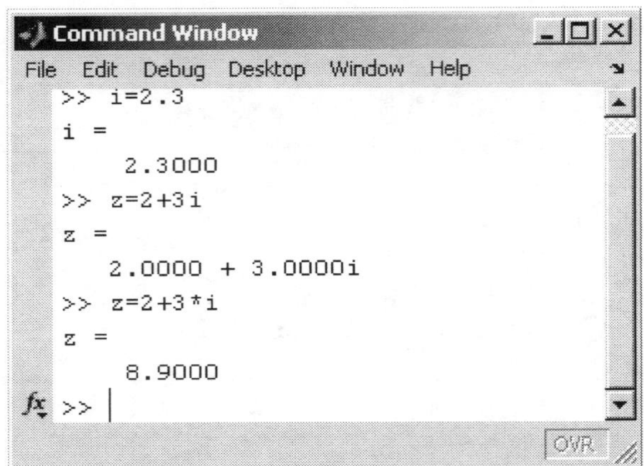

Command Window
File Edit Debug Desktop Window Help
>> i=2.3
i =
2.3000
>> z=2+3i
z =
2.0000 + 3.0000i
>> z=2+3*i
z =
8.9000
>>
OVR


**Figure 2.2.2**

## Example 2.2.2-1

Given $zz = 1.9\,e^{(3.5-0.3i)} + (2-5i)$, Find:

a. $zz$ in Rectangular (Standard) Form
b. (angle), arg($zz$)
c. Re($zz$)
d. Im($zz$)
e. mod($zz$) (absolute value function recognizes a complex argument)
f. conj($zz$)

The MATLAB session is

```
Command Window
File  Edit  Debug  Desktop  Window  Help
>> zz=1.9*exp(3.5-0.3i)+(2-5i)
zz =
  62.1092 -23.5939i
>> angle(zz)
ans =
   -0.3630
>> real(zz)
ans =
   62.1092
>> imag(zz)
ans =
  -23.5939
>> abs(zz)
ans =
   66.4396
>> conj(zz)
ans =
  62.1092 +23.5939i
>>
OVR
```

## Example 2.2.2-2

Find all the roots of $z^4 + 4iz = 0$ using the `roots(x)` function.

This function finds the roots of polynomials where x is a vector of the coefficients. The first element of the vector must be the coefficient of the highest order term and zero placeholders must be included for any missing terms. The last element will be the constant term, if any. The polynomial above illustrates this requirement:

```
Command Window
File Edit Debug Desktop Window Help
>> v=[1 0 0 -4i 0]
v =
   1.0000          0          0          0 - 4.0000i          0
>> roots(v)
ans =
        0
  -1.3747 + 0.7937i
  -0.0000 - 1.5874i
   1.3747 + 0.7937i
>>
```

## 2.2.3 Programming in MATLAB

These examples demonstrate how to use the Script and Function Editor in MATLAB. Create a new script file by selecting File | New | Script (or Cntl-N). The first line should be a comment with the program name. Program names can be any legal MATLAB variable name, but be careful not to use the existing MATLAB command or function names as these will be overridden. Also, recall that certain commands are reserved and cannot be used as variable names. File names will automatically be given the extension "m"; hence, these are referred to as "m-files".

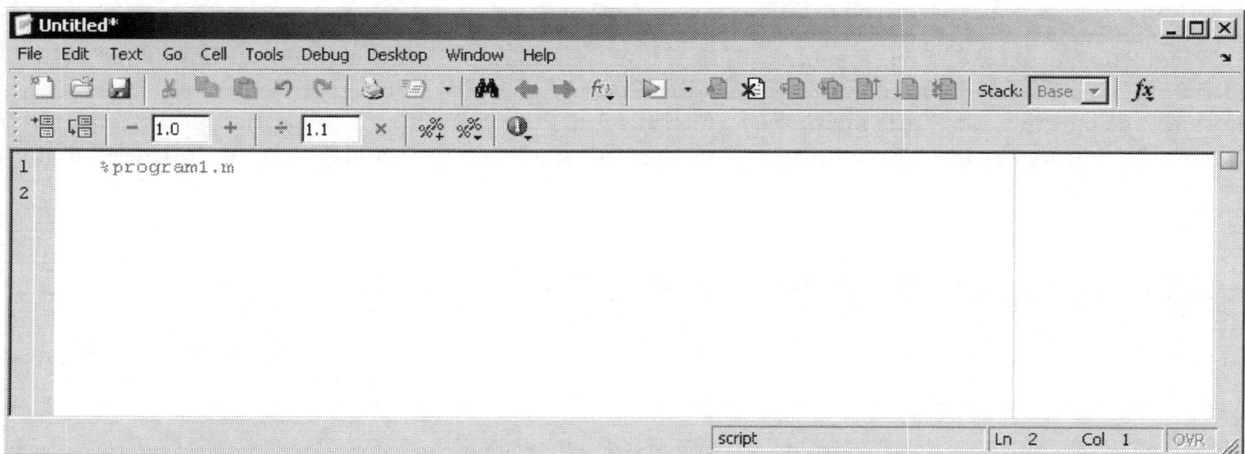


Function programs can be created by selecting File | New | Function. The first line of the file *must be* the function definition line as shown in Figure 2.2.3

MATLAB conveniently creates the necessary syntax to insert the output and input arguments, as well as the function name. The function name can also be any legal MATLAB variable and the same caveat applies about overriding existing command names. CAUTION: Always save the function m-file with the same name as that of the function, otherwise this will lead to confusion. When the function is invoked, MATLAB will look for the m-file name in the current path, not the function name.

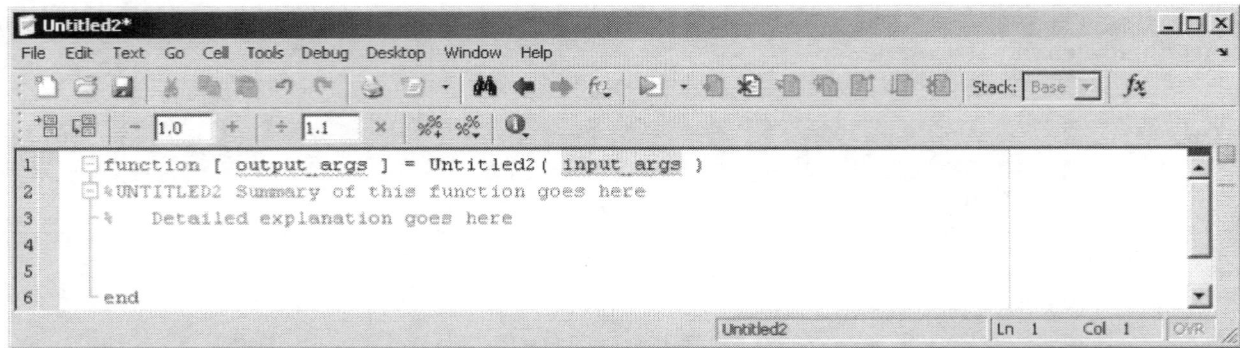


A word about Comments: Many programmers only add minimal comments or skip this important step altogether. Comments describe the code operation in simple terms and facilitates debugging and understanding. Many times, a special function will be written and then go unused for some time. When the user wants to use the function, it would be nice if there was some description of what the input arguments are, the units needed (if any), what the function does (!), and the results that are returned.

In MATLAB m-files, comments are included by starting a line with `(%)`. Any text following the % will be ignored, so the programmer can freely enter any information. This can be a stand-alone line, or added at the end of a command line. Example comments are included in the examples below.

Adding comments as the first lines of any Script m-file are particularly helpful, because MATLAB displays these lines when the `help filename` command is invoked. All comments down to the first executable line are displayed to help the user discern the purpose of the command. For a Function m-file, comment lines appearing immediately after the function definition line, and down to the first executable line, are displayed when `help` is invoked.

The H1 comment line: The very first comment line is special. When the command `lookfor abcxyz` is invoked, MATLAB searches all files for the string "abcxyz" in the H1 comment line and displays the filename where this string is found. It would be good to get into the habit of including a keyword, name, or other description in user m-files, especially function commands, to facilitate searches (Figure 2.2.4).

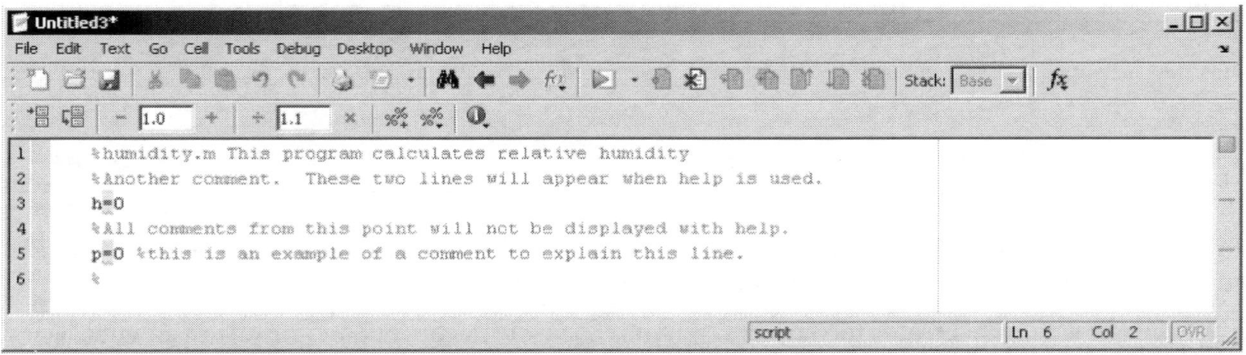

## Example 2.2.3-1

Create a program in MATLAB to display the first 10 numbers of the Fibonacci series:

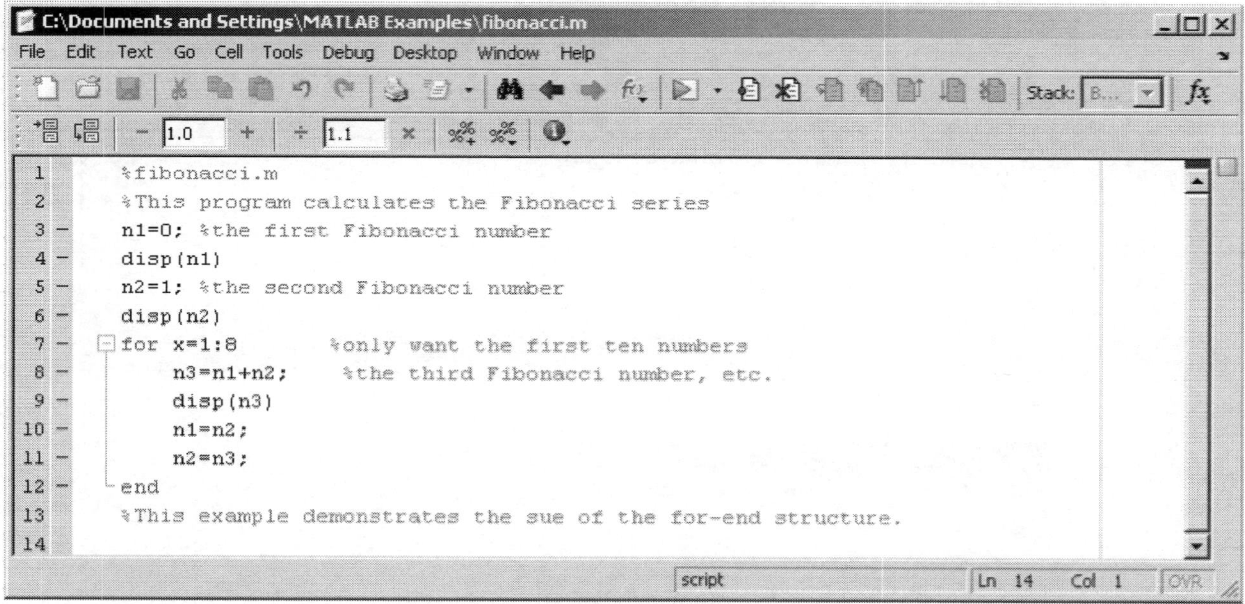
C:\Documents and Settings\MATLAB Examples\fibonacci.m
File Edit Text Go Cell Tools Debug Desktop Window Help
%fibonacci.m
%This program calculates the Fibonacci series
n1=0; %the first Fibonacci number
disp(n1)
n2=1; %the second Fibonacci number
disp(n2)
for x=1:8 %only want the first ten numbers
n3=n1+n2; %the third Fibonacci number, etc.
disp(n3)
n1=n2;
n2=n3;
end
%This example demonstrates the sue of the for-end structure.
script
Ln 14 Col 1 OVR

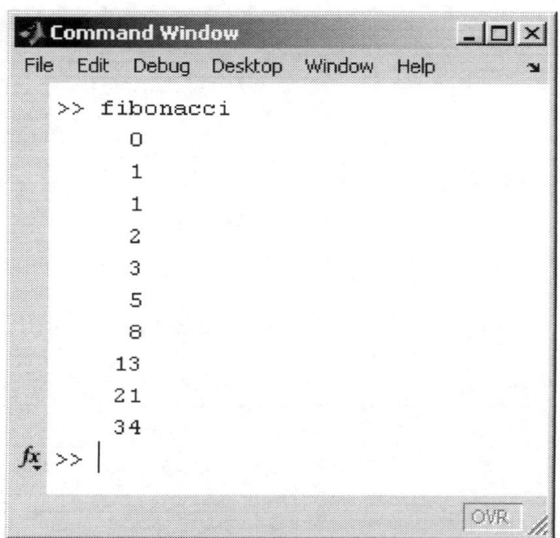
Command Window
File Edit Debug Desktop Window Help
>> fibonacci
0
1
1
2
3
5
8
13
21
34
>>
OVR

## Example 2.2.3-2

Create a function program to find the volume of a sphere for any radius, where $\text{Vol} = \frac{4}{3}\pi r^3$.

C:\Documents and Settings\MATLAB Examples\volsph.m

```
function [volume] = volsph(radius)
%This function finds the volume of a sphere,
% if the radius is known.
volume=(4/3)*pi*radius^3;
end
```

volsph Ln 4 Col 26 OVR

Command Window

```
>> r=4.3
r =
    4.3000
>> vol=volsph(r)
vol =
  333.0381
>> %note that the variables 'volume' and 'radius'
>> %do not appear in the Workspace, because
>> %they are "local" to the function only.
```

## Example 2.2.3-3

Create a function program in MATLAB that solves the ***signum*** function.

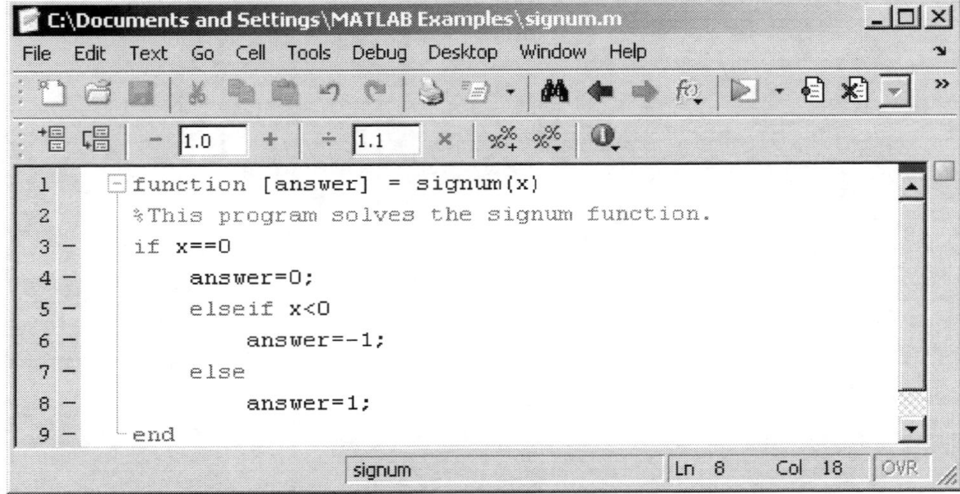
C:\Documents and Settings\MATLAB Examples\signum.m
File Edit Text Go Cell Tools Debug Desktop Window Help
function [answer] = signum(x)
%This program solves the signum function.
if x==0
answer=0;
elseif x<0
answer=-1;
else
answer=1;
end
signum
Ln 8 Col 18
OVR

```
Command Window
File Edit Debug Desktop Window Help
>> nbr=-3
nbr =
    -3
>> sgn=signum(nbr)
sgn =
    -1
>> nbr=5
nbr =
     5
>> sgn=signum(nbr)
sgn =
     1
>> nbr=0
nbr =
     0
>> sgn=signum(nbr)
sgn =
     0
>> %It is good practice to test all logic paths.
```

## Example 2.2.3-4

MATLAB functions also allow multiple output results as well as multiple variables in the input argument list. The syntax is `[a b c]=fcnname(x,y,z)`. Create a function program in MATLAB that returns the volume and surface area of a cylinder when given the height and radius. The governing equations are

$$Vol_{CYL} = \pi * r^2 * h \qquad SArea_{CYL} = (2 * \pi * r^2) + (2 * \pi * r * h)$$

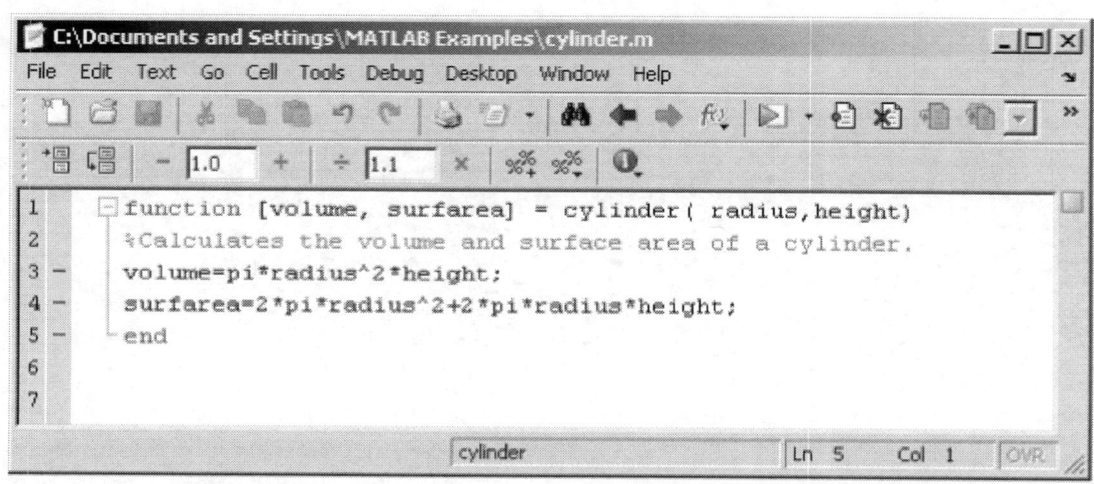

C:\Documents and Settings\MATLAB Examples\cylinder.m
File Edit Text Go Cell Tools Debug Desktop Window Help
1.0
1.1
function [volume, surfarea] = cylinder( radius,height)
%Calculates the volume and surface area of a cylinder.
volume=pi*radius^2*height;
surfarea=2*pi*radius^2+2*pi*radius*height;
end
cylinder
Ln 5 Col 1
OVR

```
>> r=2.3
r =
    2.3000
>> h=4.7
h =
    4.7000
>> [vol sa]=cylinder(r,h)
vol =
   78.1094
sa =
  101.1593
>> %note that the function returns multiple values,
>> %and a vector assignment must be made to capture
>> %both values.  If only one variable is used,
>> %the second value is lost:
>> cyl=cylinder(r,h)
cyl =
   78.1094
>>
```

## 2.2.4 Solving Systems of Linear Equations in MATLAB

Many types of physical systems are represented by a system of linear equations. When the number of independent equations equals the number of unknowns, a unique solution may be found.

### Example 2.2.4-1 Solve the following system of equations for [*x*, *y*, *z*].

$$x - 2y + 3z = 2$$
$$2x + y - 7z = 6 \quad \text{convert to matrix form}$$
$$x - y - z = 1$$

$$\begin{bmatrix} 1 & -2 & 3 \\ 2 & 1 & -7 \\ 1 & -1 & -1 \end{bmatrix} \begin{bmatrix} x \\ y \\ z \end{bmatrix} = \begin{bmatrix} 2 \\ 6 \\ 1 \end{bmatrix}$$

The solution is $\bar{x} = A^{-1} * \bar{\mathbf{d}}$

```
>> A=[1 -2 3;2 1 -7;1 -1 -1]
A =
     1    -2     3
     2     1    -7
     1    -1    -1
>> d=[2;6;1]
d =
     2
     6
     1
>> x=A^-1*d
x =
    5.0000
    3.0000
    1.0000
>> x=inv(A)*d
x =
    5.0000
    3.0000
    1.0000
>>
```

## Example 2.2.4-2

The electric circuit from Example 1.2.4-2 is solved using MATLAB. The matrix equation is

$$\begin{bmatrix} (R_1+R_2+R_3) & -R_2 & -R_3 \\ -R_2 & (R_2+R_4+R_6) & -R_6 \\ -R_3 & -R_6 & (R_3+R_5+R_6) \end{bmatrix} \begin{bmatrix} i_1 \\ i_2 \\ i_3 \end{bmatrix} = \begin{bmatrix} V_1 \\ 0 \\ 0 \end{bmatrix}$$

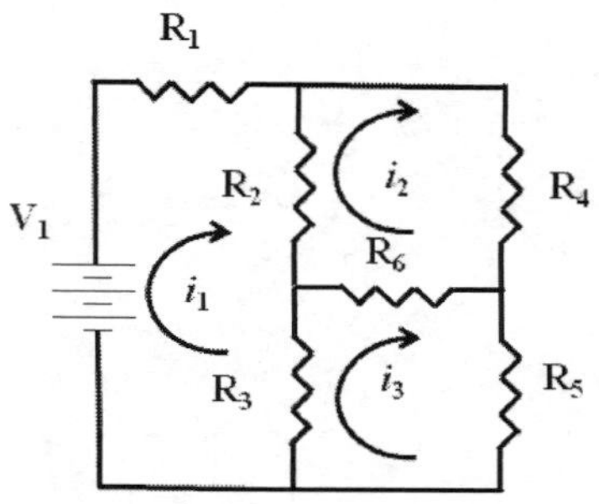


The values are

$$R_1 = 5\Omega \quad R_2 = 15\Omega \quad R_3 = 8\Omega \quad R_4 = 10\Omega \quad R_5 = 7\Omega \quad R_6 = 12\Omega \quad V_1 = 9V$$

And then substituting for the given values of $R$'s and $V_1$, the MATLAB session is

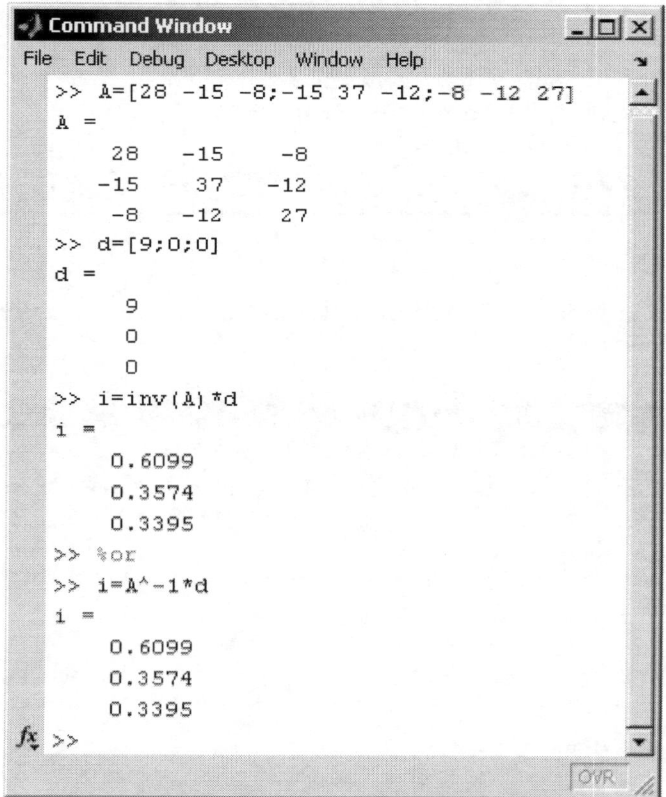


## Example 2.2.4-3

Solving systems of linear equations by Gaussian elimination.

Unlike the TI-89, MATLAB only has the `rref(augmat)` function to produce the Reduced Row Echelon Form. This is convenient because the resulting matrix displays the solution directly. An "augmented matrix" is required as an argument, which is created by appending the $\bar{d}$ vector to the coefficient matrix $A$, using the append operation in MATLAB. Using the equations from Example 2.2.4-1, the MATLAB session to create the augmented matrix and the `rref()` solution is

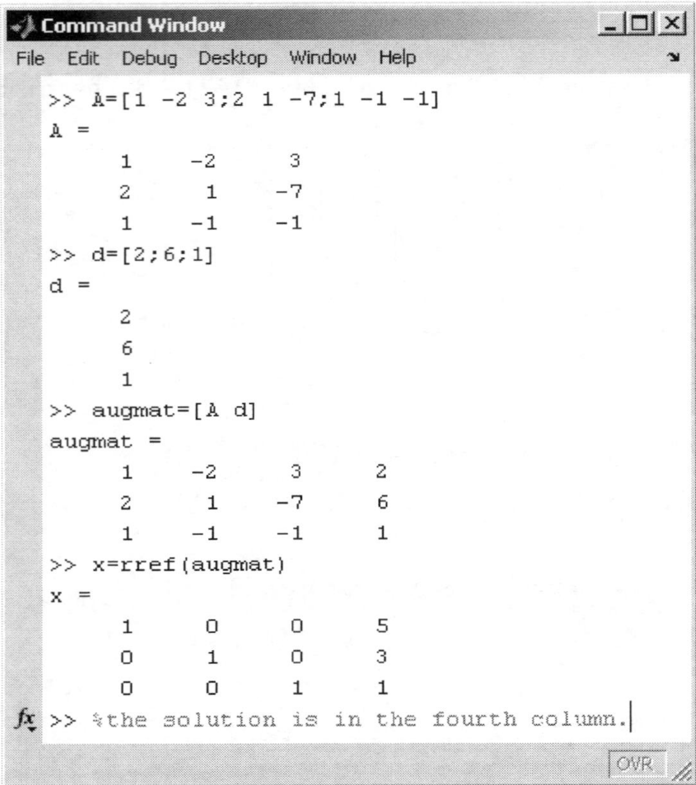

Command Window
File Edit Debug Desktop Window Help
>> A=[1 -2 3;2 1 -7;1 -1 -1]
A =
1 -2 3
2 1 -7
1 -1 -1
>> d=[2;6;1]
d =
2
6
1
>> augmat=[A d]
augmat =
1 -2 3 2
2 1 -7 6
1 -1 -1 1
>> x=rref(augmat)
x =
1 0 0 5
0 1 0 3
0 0 1 1
>> %the solution is in the fourth column.
OVR


MATLAB also performs Gaussian elimination with the "left divide operator (\)":

Command Window

File Edit Debug Desktop Window Help

```
>> %using the same variables in the Workspace:
>> A
A =
     1    -2     3
     2     1    -7
     1    -1    -1
>> d
d =
     2
     6
     1
>> x=A\d
x =
    5.0000
    3.0000
    1.0000
>>
```

OVR

## Example 2.2.4-4 Infinite solutions to linear systems.

Consider the equation of the straight-line $y = 3x + 2$. This is the form of slope = 3, and $y$-intercept = 2. For matrix algebra, this equation is normally arranged to have all the unknown variables on the left side of the equation, thus $-3x + y = 2$.

What is the solution to this linear equation? In other words, is there a point unique to the "system"? No, because this is a straight-line, there are infinite solutions. For every $x$, there is a $y$, but there are an infinite number of $x$'s.

Consider the plot of this line on a Cartesian coordinate system. Observe that there are two "solutions" at $x = 0$ and $y = 0$. In fact, if we perform the left divide operation in MATLAB to solve Ax=b, we get one of these solutions:

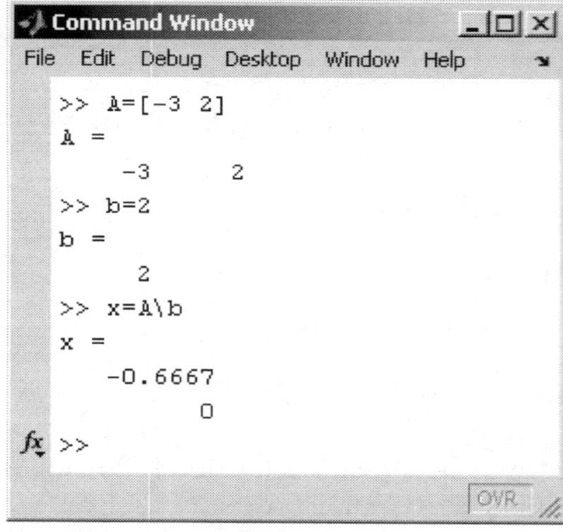


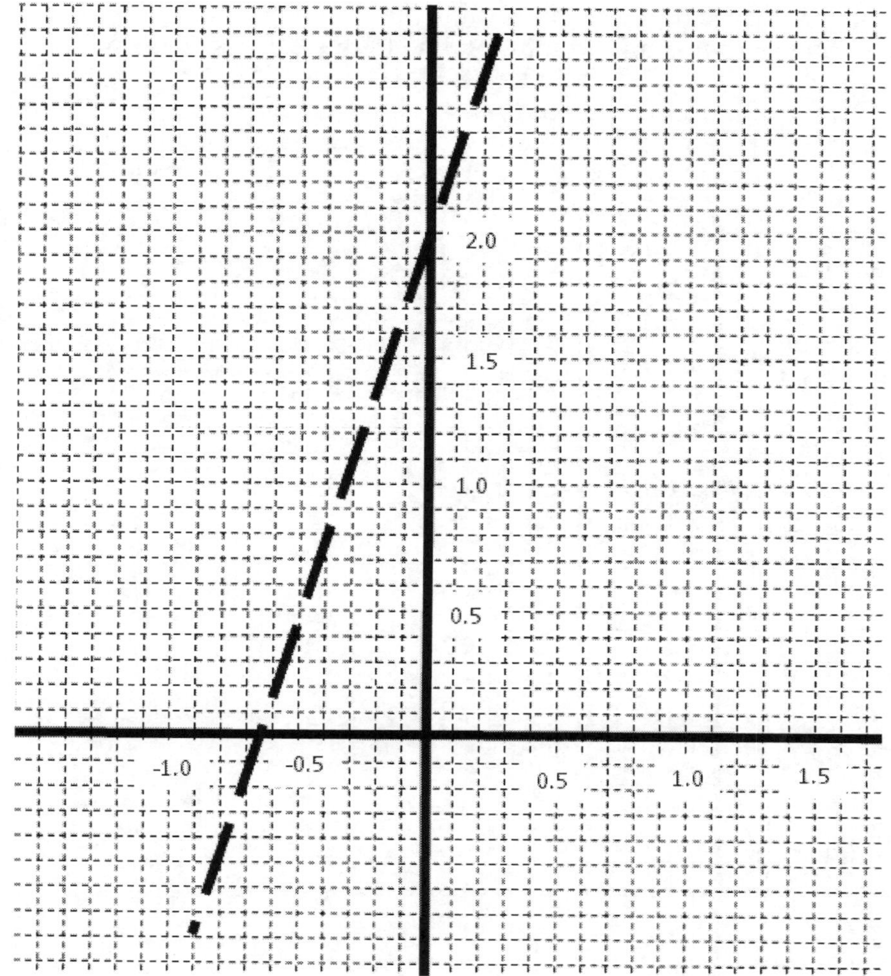

Now consider two lines, the original equation and a new line $-6x+2y=4$, which is just the original line multiplied by 2. This is a second-order "system of linear equations" in matrix form:

$\begin{bmatrix}-3 & 1\\ -6 & 2\end{bmatrix} * \begin{bmatrix}x\\ y\end{bmatrix} = \begin{bmatrix}2\\ 4\end{bmatrix}$. It should be obvious that $\det(A)=0$, which means there is not a unique solution. The augmented matrix is $\begin{bmatrix}-3 & 1 & 2\\ -6 & 2 & 4\end{bmatrix}$ and Gaussian elimination gives

```
Command Window
File  Edit  Debug  Desktop  Window  Help
>> Aaug=[-3 1 2;-6 2 4]
Aaug =
    -3     1     2
    -6     2     4
>> rref(Aaug)
ans =
    1.0000   -0.3333   -0.6667
         0         0         0
fx >>
OVR
```

Recognize that the result of all 0s in Row 2 indicates an infinite solution, a straight-line. The normal matrix equation $\overline{x} = A^{-1} * \overline{b}$ cannot be solved (why not?). But there is a MATLAB function called `pinv()` for "pseudoinverse", which provides a solution for a unique point on the straight-line. That point is the *Euclidean Norm*, which is the closest point on the line to the Origin (i.e., the shortest perpendicular line from the infinite solution line to the origin). In MATLAB:

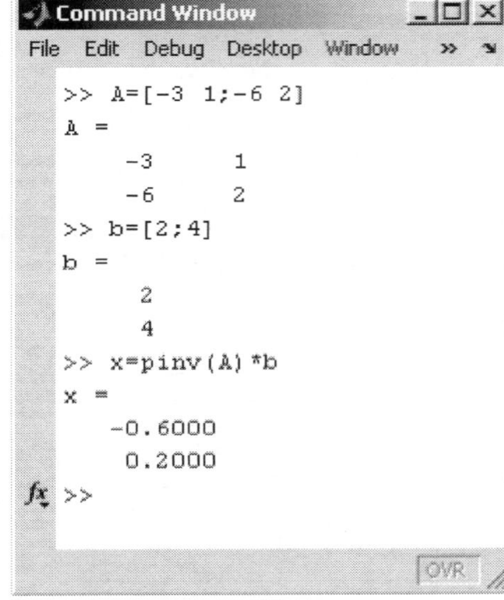


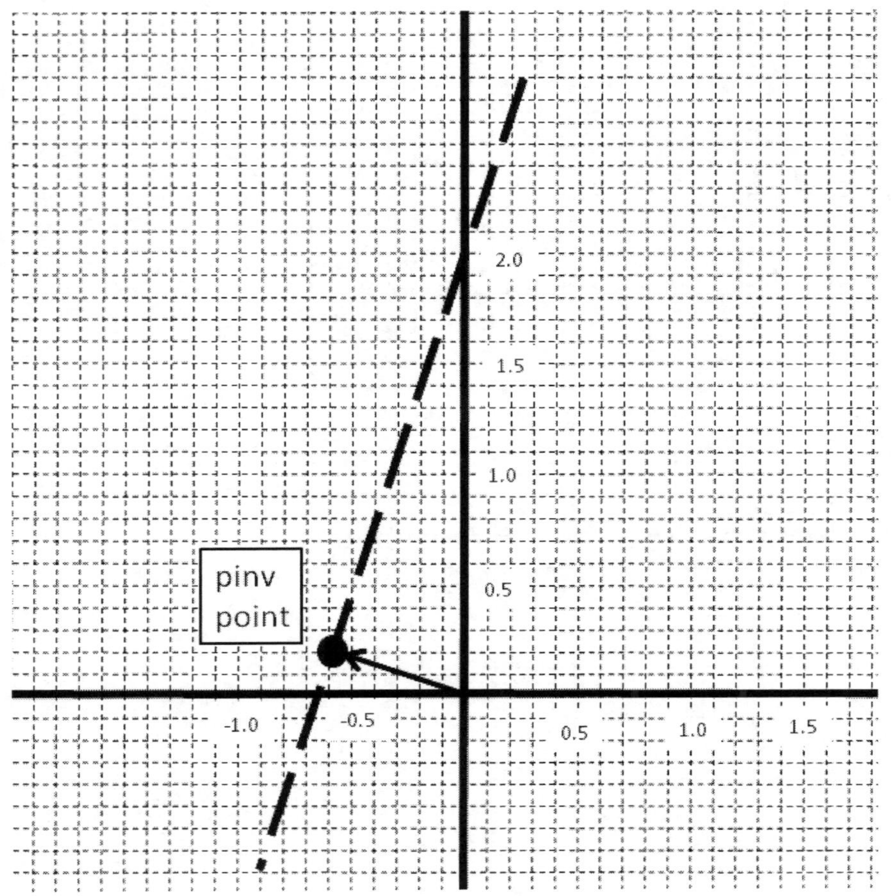

The solution (–0.6,0.2) is the point on the line closest to the origin.

Now extrapolate this thinking to three dimensions. Three equations of a third-order linear system representing an infinite solution all intersect at a straight-line. The solution is the equation of a line in terms of one of the variables, for example $x$. There are an infinite number of $(x,y,z)$ coordinates on the solution line, but by defining a value for $x$ defines values for $y$ and $z$, and a unique point is defined. In MATLAB, the `pinv()` function defines that unique point as being the closest point on the solution line to the origin.

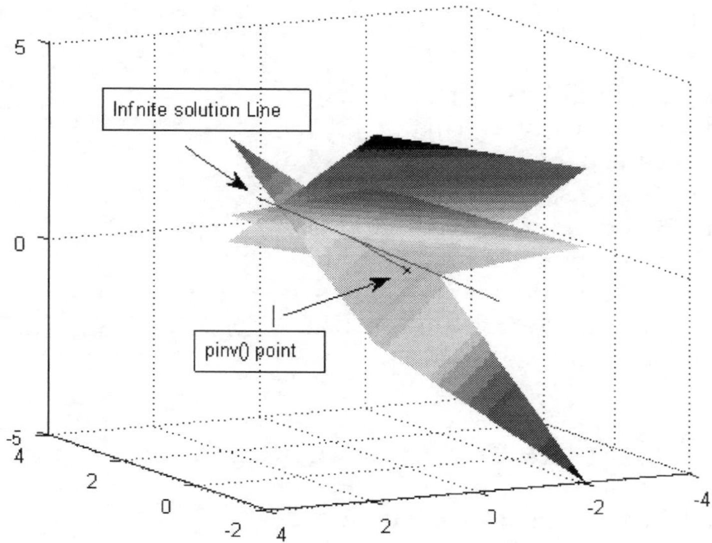


## Example 2.2.4-5

An infinite solution system. Consider the following system of linear equations:

$$x + y - z = 1$$
$$3x - y + 3z = 5$$
$$x - y + 2z = 2$$

The matrix equation is

$$\begin{bmatrix} 1 & 1 & -1 \\ 3 & -1 & 3 \\ 1 & -1 & 2 \end{bmatrix} \begin{bmatrix} x \\ y \\ z \end{bmatrix} = \begin{bmatrix} 1 \\ 5 \\ 2 \end{bmatrix}$$

And the augmented matrix is

$$\begin{bmatrix} A & b \end{bmatrix} = \begin{bmatrix} 1 & 1 & -1 & 1 \\ 3 & -1 & 3 & 5 \\ 1 & -1 & 2 & 2 \end{bmatrix}$$

Note that det($A$) = 0, and so the inverse does not exist; therefore, a unique solution does not exist. Gaussian elimination reveals the following result:

Command Window

File Edit Debug Desktop Window Help

```
>> A=[1 1 -1;3 -1 3;1 -1 2]
A =
     1     1    -1
     3    -1     3
     1    -1     2
>> b=[1;5;2]
b =
     1
     5
     2
>> det(A)
ans =
     0
>> rref([A b])
ans =
    1.0000         0    0.5000    1.5000
         0    1.0000   -1.5000   -0.5000
         0         0         0         0
fx >>
```

OVR

An infinite solution is suggested by the third row of the Row Echelon Form. This implies that $0 * z = 0$ or that $z$ can have infinite values. A parametric equation can be produced by

$$\begin{bmatrix} x \\ y \\ z \end{bmatrix} = \begin{bmatrix} \frac{3}{2} - \frac{1}{2}\lambda \\ -\frac{1}{2} + \frac{3}{2}\lambda \\ \lambda \end{bmatrix}$$

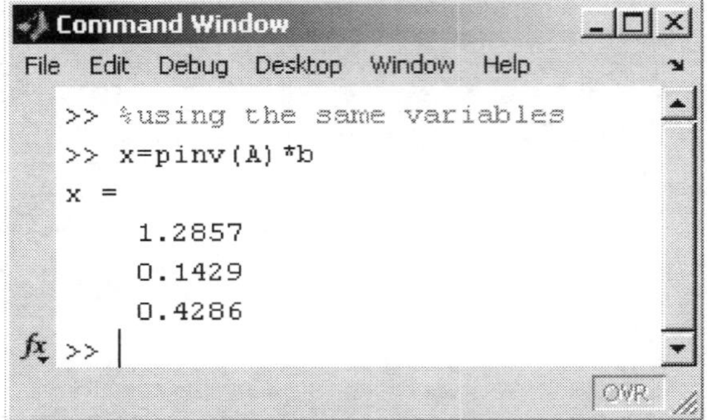


letting $z = \lambda$ and backward substituting for $z$ to obtain expressions for $x$ and $y$ in terms of $z$. This gives a result which happens to be the parametric equation of a straight-line in three dimensions, as shown in Example 2.2.4-4. The MATLAB pseudoinverse solution is shown in Figure 2.2.5 This solution is a unique point in the 3D Cartesian system that is the point of closest approach to the origin of the infinite line solution. See the figure in Example 2.2.4-4

## Example 2.2.4-6. Using the `rank()` function.

Using the system of linear equations from Example 2.2.4-1,

As the determinant is not 0, and the rank of the coefficient matrix $A$ is equal to the number of unknowns ($n = 3$), matrix $A$ represents three independent equations. The rank of the augmented matrix is also equal to the number of unknowns. Meeting these three conditions indicates a system with a unique solution.

```
Command Window
File Edit Debug Desktop Window Help
>> A
A =
     1    -2     3
     2     1    -7
     1    -1     1
>> d
d =
     2
     6
     1
>> det(A)
ans =
    3.0000
>> rank(A)
ans =
     3
>> rank([A d])
ans =
     3
>>
```

```
Command Window
File Edit Debug Desktop Window Help
>> A
A =
     1     1    -1
     3    -1     3
     1    -1     2
>> b
b =
     1
     5
     2
>> det(A)
ans =
     0
>> rank(A)
ans =
     2
>> rank([A b])
ans =
     2
>>
```

Compare this result to the system of Example 2.2.4-1

For Example 2.2.4-5, as the determinant is 0, a unique solution does not exist. The rank of the coefficient matrix $A$ is less than $n$ = 3, indicating fewer independent equations than unknowns. However, since *rank(A)=rank([A b])*, an infinite solution exists, represented by a straight-line in three dimensions.

If $rank(A) \neq rank([A\ b])$ then the system is under or over determined, and no solution exists.

## Example 2.2.4-7

Given the truss system with the loadings in the figure shown below, solve for the 11 unknown forces and the 3 unknown external reactions. Since there are seven pin joints, the theory of truss analysis can generate 14 independent equations to solve for the 14 unknowns. Find the solution using both the matrix inverse and the Gaussian elimination methods.

The equations are:

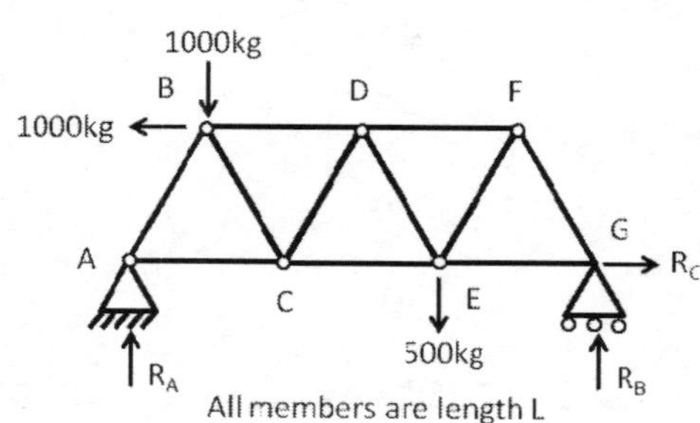


$$R_A + T_{AB}\sin\theta = 0$$
$$T_{AB}\cos\theta + T_{AC} = 0$$
$$-T_{AB}\sin\theta - T_{BC}\sin\theta - 1000 = 0$$
$$-T_{AB}\cos\theta + T_{BC}\cos\theta + T_{BD} - 1000 = 0$$
$$T_{BC}\sin\theta + T_{CD}\sin\theta = 0$$
$$-T_{AC} - T_{BC}\cos\theta + T_{CD}\cos\theta + T_{CE} = 0$$
$$-T_{DC}\sin\theta - T_{DE}\sin\theta = 0$$
$$-T_{BD} - T_{CD}\cos\theta + T_{DE}\cos\theta + T_{DF} = 0$$
$$T_{ED}\sin\theta + T_{EF}\sin\theta - 500 = 0$$
$$-T_{EC} - T_{ED}\cos\theta + T_{EF}\cos\theta + T_{AB} = 0$$
$$-T_{EF}\sin\theta - T_{FG}\sin\theta = 0$$
$$-T_{DF} - T_{EF}\cos\theta + T_{FG}\cos\theta = 0$$
$$R_B - T_{FG}\sin\theta = 0$$
$$R_C - T_{EG} - T_{FG}\cos\theta = 0$$

And in matrix form:

$$\begin{bmatrix}
1 & 0 & 0 & \sin\theta & 0 & 0 & 0 & 0 & 0 & 0 & 0 & 0 & 0 & 0 \\
0 & 0 & 0 & \cos\theta & 1 & 0 & 0 & 0 & 0 & 0 & 0 & 0 & 0 & 0 \\
0 & 0 & 0 & -\sin\theta & -\sin\theta & 0 & 0 & 0 & 0 & 0 & 0 & 0 & 0 & 0 \\
0 & 0 & 0 & -\cos\theta & 0 & \cos\theta & 1 & 0 & 0 & 0 & 0 & 0 & 0 & 0 \\
0 & 0 & 0 & 0 & 0 & \sin\theta & 0 & \sin\theta & 0 & 0 & 0 & 0 & 0 & 0 \\
0 & 0 & 0 & 0 & -1 & -\cos\theta & 0 & \cos\theta & 1 & 0 & 0 & 0 & 0 & 0 \\
0 & 0 & 0 & 0 & 0 & 0 & 0 & 0 & -\sin\theta & 0 & -\sin\theta & 0 & 0 & 0 \\
0 & 0 & 0 & 0 & 0 & 0 & -1 & \cos\theta & 0 & \cos\theta & 1 & 0 & 0 & 0 \\
0 & 0 & 0 & 0 & 0 & 0 & 0 & 0 & 0 & \sin\theta & 0 & \sin\theta & 0 & 0 \\
0 & 0 & 0 & 0 & 0 & 0 & 0 & 0 & -1 & -\cos\theta & 0 & \cos\theta & 1 & 0 \\
0 & 0 & 0 & 0 & 0 & 0 & 0 & 0 & 0 & 0 & 0 & -1 & 0 & -1 \\
0 & 0 & 0 & 0 & 0 & 0 & 0 & 0 & 0 & 0 & -1 & \cos\theta & 0 & \cos\theta \\
0 & 1 & 0 & 0 & 0 & 0 & 0 & 0 & 0 & 0 & 0 & 0 & 0 & \sin\theta \\
0 & 0 & 1 & 0 & 0 & 0 & 0 & 0 & 0 & 0 & 0 & 0 & -1 & -\cos\theta
\end{bmatrix}
\begin{bmatrix} R_A \\ R_B \\ R_C \\ T_{AB} \\ T_{AC} \\ T_{BC} \\ T_{BD} \\ T_{CD} \\ T_{CE} \\ T_{DE} \\ T_{DF} \\ T_{EF} \\ T_{EG} \\ T_{FG} \end{bmatrix}
=
\begin{bmatrix} 0 \\ 0 \\ 1000 \\ 1000 \\ 0 \\ 0 \\ 0 \\ 0 \\ 500 \\ 0 \\ 0 \\ 0 \\ 0 \\ 0 \end{bmatrix}$$

The matrix solution is $\bar{x} = A^{-1} * \bar{\mathbf{d}}$

```
>> x=A^-1*d
x =
        2000.00
         767.95
       -1041.45
       -2309.40
        1154.70
       -1154.70
         422.65
        1154.70
          -0.00
        -309.40
           0.00
         886.75
        -598.08
        -886.75
>>
```

The Gaussian elimination solution is

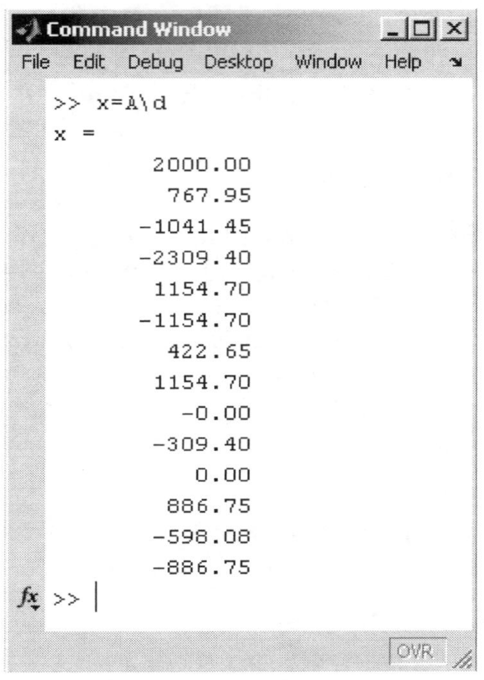


## 2.2.5 Creating Plots (Graphs) with MATLAB Script Files

MATLAB provides a number of line commands for creating and labeling graphs. These commands can be used from the Command Line prompt (>>), or in m-files.

### Example 2.2.5-1

Create a graph of the $y = \exp(-0.5 * x) * \sin(x)$ function, from $0 - 2\pi$, and label the $x$ and $y$ axes.

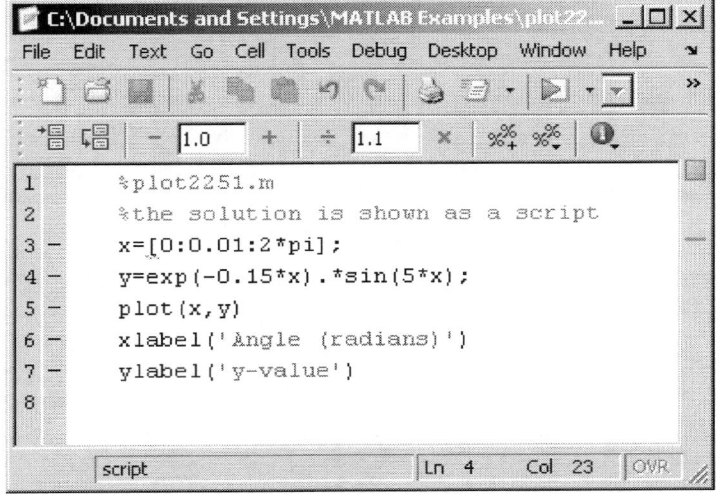

C:\Documents and Settings\MATLAB Examples\plot22...
File Edit Text Go Cell Tools Debug Desktop Window Help
1.0
1.1
%plot2251.m
%the solution is shown as a script
x=[0:0.01:2*pi];
y=exp(-0.15*x).*sin(5*x);
plot(x,y)
xlabel('Angle (radians)')
ylabel('y-value')
script
Ln 4
Col 23
OVR

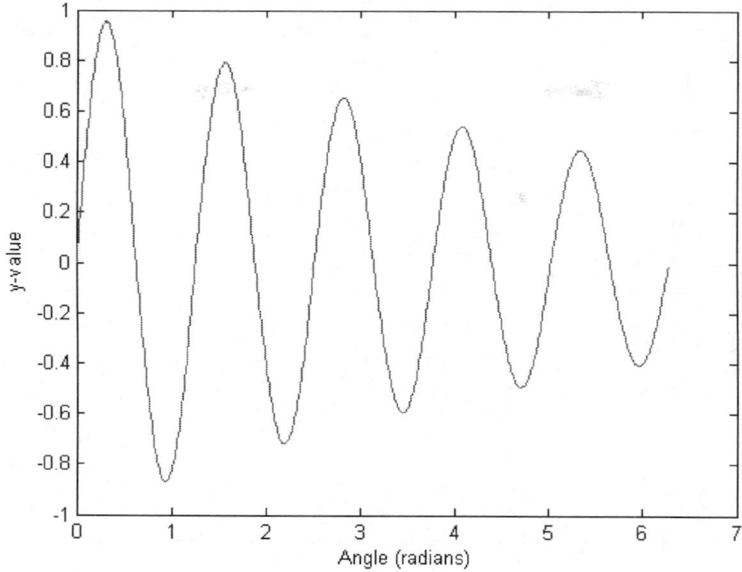
1
0.8
0.6
0.4
0.2
0
-0.2
-0.4
-0.6
-0.8
-1
y-value
0
1
2
3
4
5
6
7
Angle (radians)

## Example 2.2.5-2

A projectile is fired from a cannon with an initial velocity of 120 m/s, at an angle of 33°. Neglecting drag, plot the altitude and velocity versus time of the flight of the projectile until it hits the ground. Label the axes, and add a title and a legend. The equations are:

$$v0y = v0 * \sin\alpha - g * t \qquad v0x = v0 * \cos\alpha \qquad h = v0 * \sin\alpha * t - 0.5 * g * t^2$$

$$time\ of\ flight = \frac{v0 * \sin\alpha}{0.5 * g} \qquad v = \sqrt{v0x^2 + v0y^2}$$

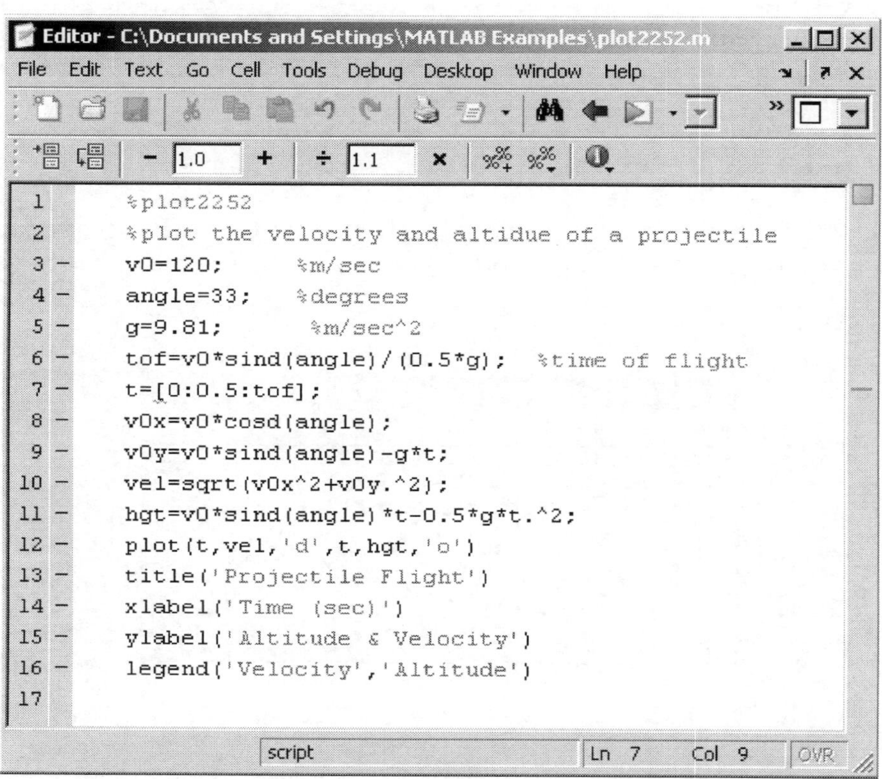
Editor - C:\Documents and Settings\MATLAB Examples\plot2252.m
File Edit Text Go Cell Tools Debug Desktop Window Help
1.0
1.1
%plot2252
%plot the velocity and altidue of a projectile
v0=120;      %m/sec
angle=33;    %degrees
g=9.81;       %m/sec^2
tof=v0*sind(angle)/(0.5*g);  %time of flight
t=[0:0.5:tof];
v0x=v0*cosd(angle);
v0y=v0*sind(angle)-g*t;
vel=sqrt(v0x^2+v0y.^2);
hgt=v0*sind(angle)*t-0.5*g*t.^2;
plot(t,vel,'d',t,hgt,'o')
title('Projectile Flight')
xlabel('Time (sec)')
ylabel('Altitude & Velocity')
legend('Velocity','Altitude')
script
Ln 7
Col 9
OVR

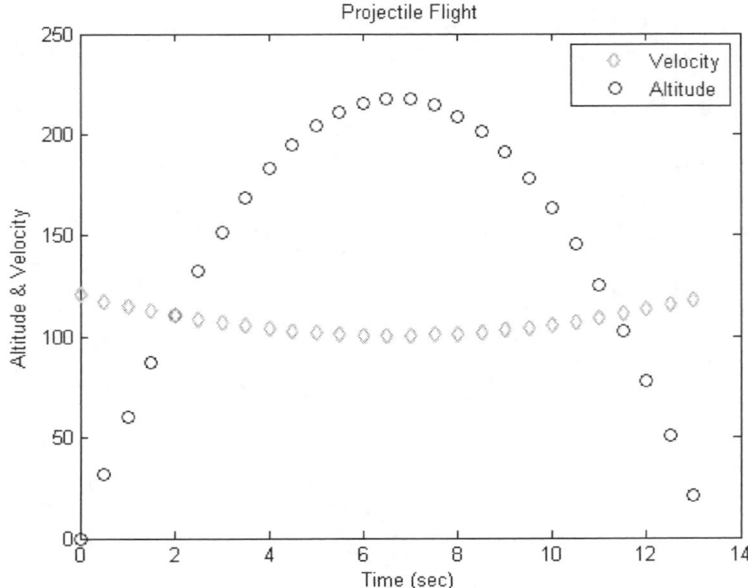


## 2.2.6 Importing Data from Sources Outside MATLAB using Script Files

The `load` and `save` commands can be used to save the contents of the MATLAB workspace, but these files cannot be used by other programs and are not discussed here. The `load` command can also be used to import ASCII text files, but MATLAB is finicky, as it expects a specific format; otherwise, it will reject the command. In addition to textual data, in many experiments, raw data are first captured and or manipulated in a spreadsheet program, such as Excel®. The results are then imported into MATLAB for special processing. The Data Import Wizard is also a handy tool and allows more flexibility when importing both of these file types. As the Wizard is an interactive tool, the reader is referred to the instructional texts.

### Example 2.2.6-1

Write a script file to import the ACSII text file called `data1.txt`, which contains the test grades of three class sections. Calculate the average grade of each section. Use the `fprintf` command to format the output.

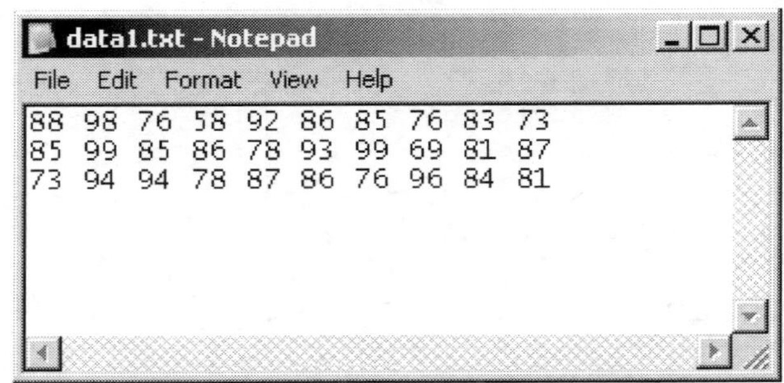

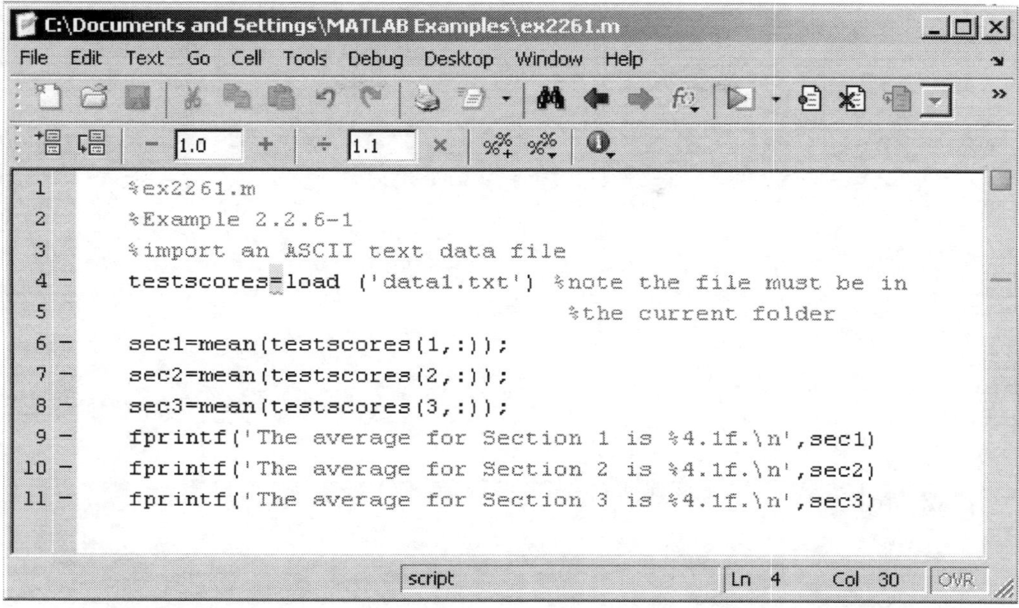


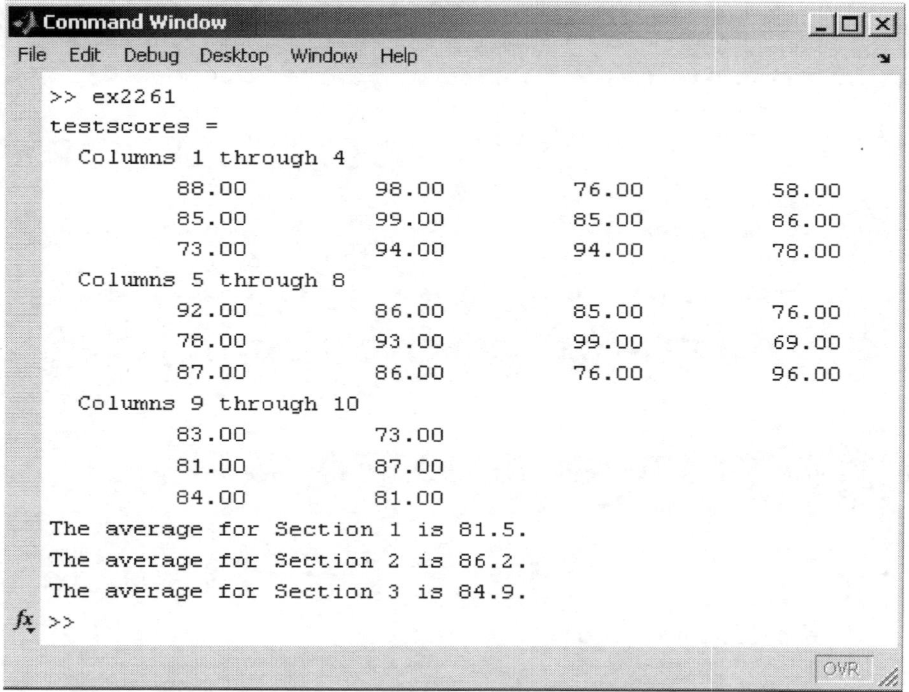


## Example 2.2.6-2

Write a script file to import the data contained in the file `xlsample.xlsx`. This data represents $x$–$y$ pairs of experimental data that is expected to show a linear response. Perform a linear regression analysis on this data to determine the equation of the line (slope and $y$-intercept), and output the results.

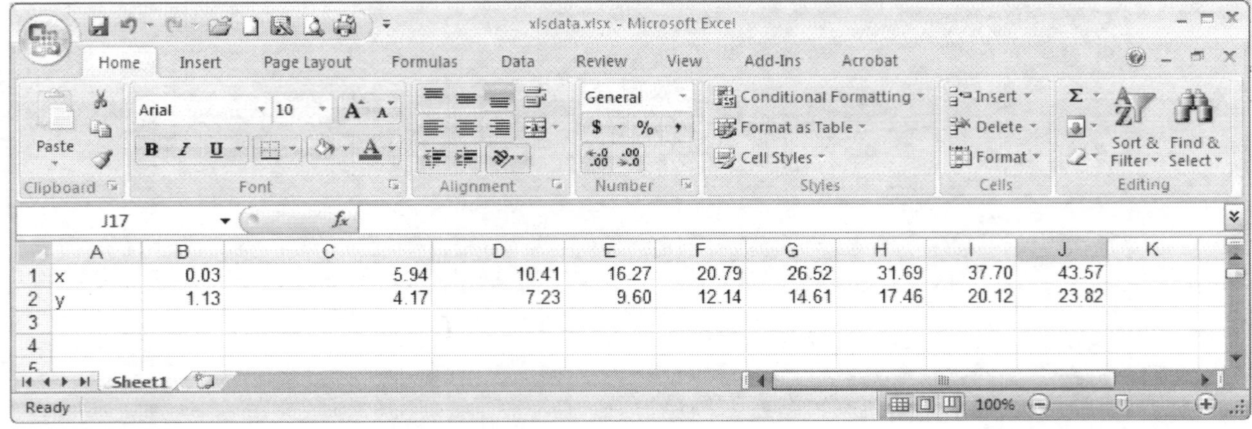
xlsdata.xlsx - Microsoft Excel
Home Insert Page Layout Formulas Data Review View Add-Ins Acrobat
J17
1 x 0.03 5.94 10.41 16.27 20.79 26.52 31.69 37.70 43.57
2 y 1.13 4.17 7.23 9.60 12.14 14.61 17.46 20.12 23.82
Sheet1
Ready

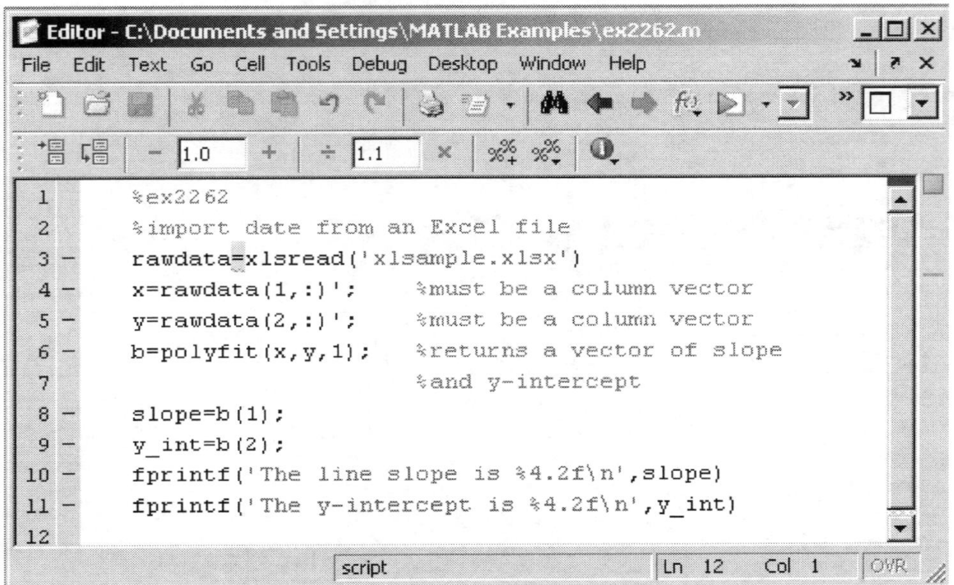
Editor - C:\Documents and Settings\MATLAB Examples\ex2262.m
File Edit Text Go Cell Tools Debug Desktop Window Help
%ex2262
%import date from an Excel file
rawdata=xlsread('xlsample.xlsx')
x=rawdata(1,:)'; %must be a column vector
y=rawdata(2,:)'; %must be a column vector
b=polyfit(x,y,1); %returns a vector of slope
%and y-intercept
slope=b(1);
y_int=b(2);
fprintf('The line slope is %4.2f\n',slope)
fprintf('The y-intercept is %4.2f\n',y_int)
script Ln 12 Col 1 OVR

Command Window

File Edit Debug Desktop Window Help

```
>> ex2262
rawdata =
  Columns 1 through 5
        0.03          5.94          10.41          16.27          20.79
        1.13          4.17           7.23           9.60          12.14
  Columns 6 through 9
       26.52         31.69          37.70          43.57
       14.61         17.46          20.12          23.82
The line slope is 0.51
The y-intercept is 1.34
>> |
```

CHAPTER 3

# Mathcad

## 3.1 Mathcad® BASICS

Mathcad® can also perform all manner of mathematical operations, and it uses a graphical user interface allowing a presentation of mathematical equations as they are normally viewed in text. While MATLAB could be considered a "program once, use many times", Mathcad is more of a "write once, use once" tool to solve a specific problem.

There are a number of good tutorial texts to get students started in Mathcad. As in the other chapters, the intent is not to replicate those tutorials, but to provide practice to improve proficiency. This chapter will help students get started, and show some shortcuts and tricks to help learn to use the tool easily.

### 3.1.1 The Mathcad Environment

Upon starting Mathcad, the user is presented with the default window view as shown in Figure 3.1.1. A discussion of the function of these windows will be left to the texts noted above.

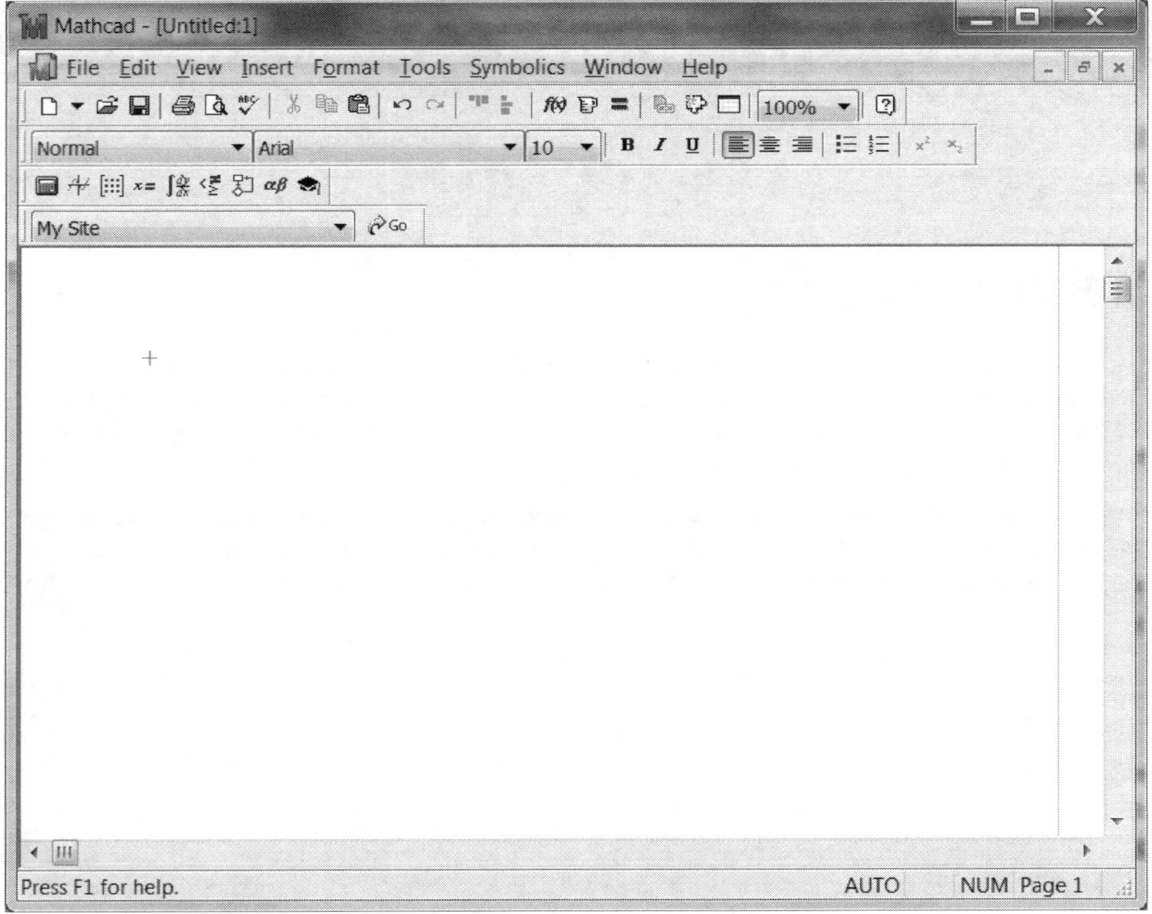


**Figure 3.1.1**

Users may create a desktop to their liking by also displaying frequently used menus, via the **View | Toolbars** pulldown menu. These graphic menus (Figure 3.1.2) remain on the desktop until closed. They give users desktop access to the most frequently used commands desired by the user.

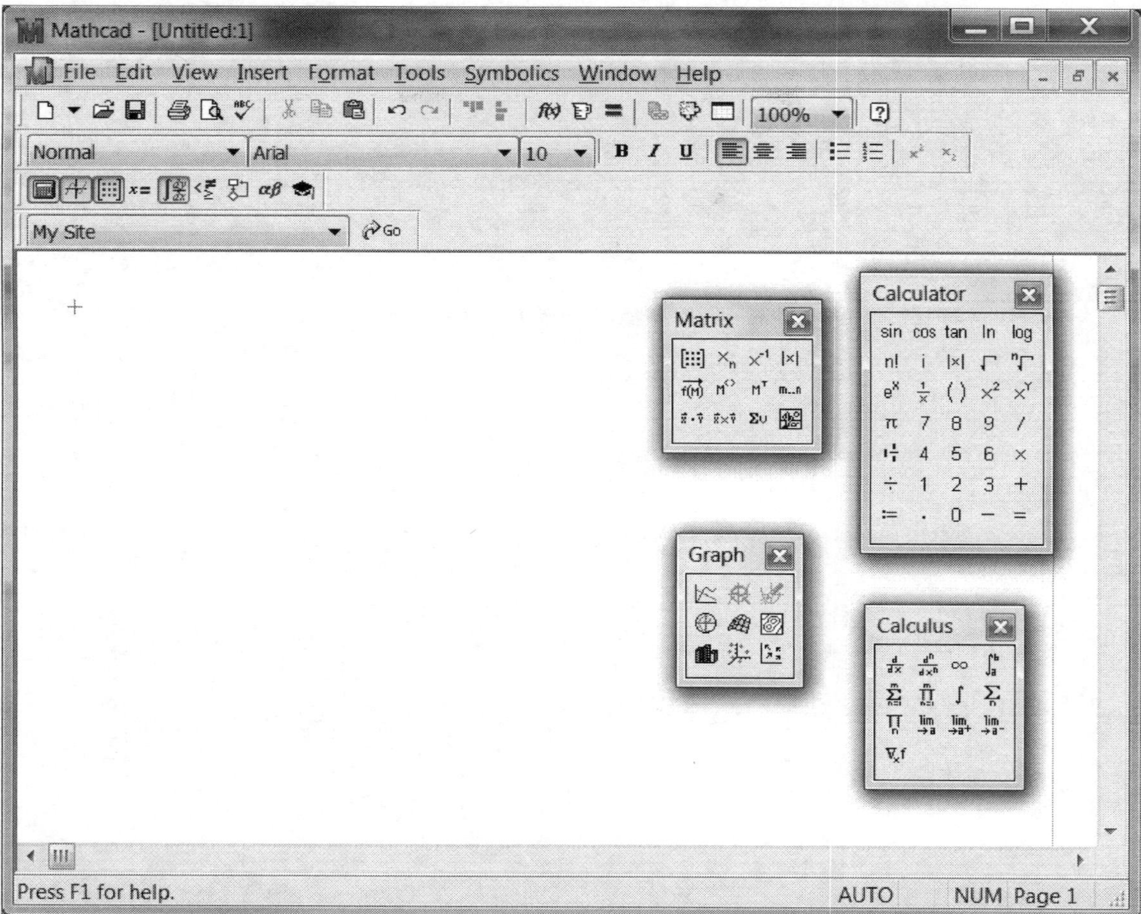


**Figure 3.1.2**

One of the most powerful features of Mathcad is the ability to combine formatted text with equations, and perform calculations at the same time. Mathcad can control margins, add headers and footers, and essentially act as a word processor in addition to calculations. This makes Mathcad an ideal tool for technical reports that include analyses for verification of designs, test results, or specifications. It also facilitates peer review of critical results required for certifications or validations. As calculations are always updated, changes or error corrections will automatically propagate through the document, and display the new results.

## 3.1.2 The Beginner's Frustration

One of the least intuitive things about Mathcad is entering equations using the keyboard. Mathcad is generally unforgiving of typing errors and corrections, does not like backspaces or deletes, and will often just not work. The equation may appear to be typed correctly, and may not even display an error, and yet it will not execute. At that point, the best thing to do is delete the entire equation and retype it.

Learning to type equations correctly requires learning how to use the space bar, and how to interpret the cursor. CAUTION: Using the space bar when typing variable names or other commands will cause the entry to be converted to "text". The font will change, and the cursor will change style and color, warning the user that this entry is now just considered plain text. As such, plain text is always considered a comment or nonexecutable command. Mathcad has default fonts for these conditions, which can be changed by the user. These are shown in Figure 3.1.3.

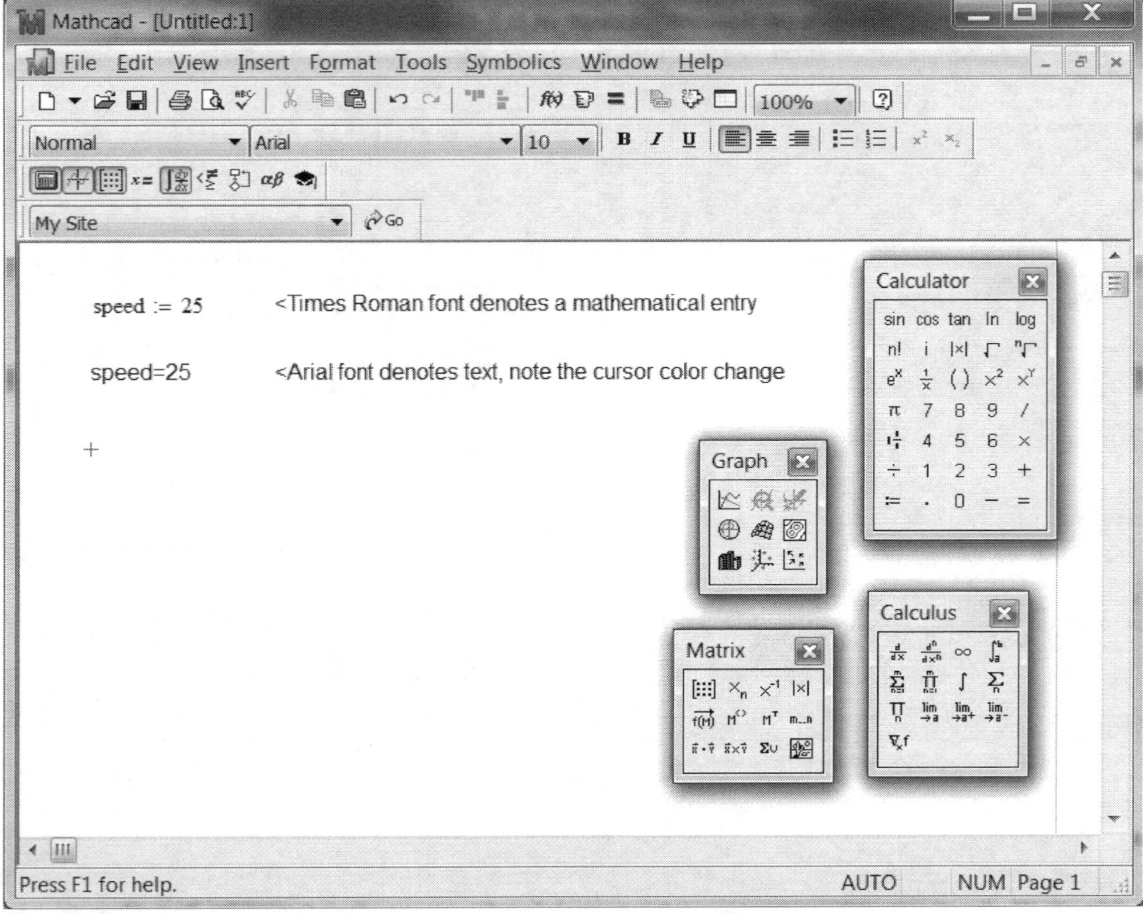


**Figure 3.1.3**

## Example 3.1.2-1 Typing exercise

Practice typing the following equation into the Mathcad workspace. When the equal sign is typed (the evaluation =), Mathcad will calculate and display the result.

$$20\log\left[\frac{\sqrt{\frac{x_0+5}{10}}}{\sqrt{x_0-5}}\right] = ? \qquad \text{for } x_0 = 8.4$$

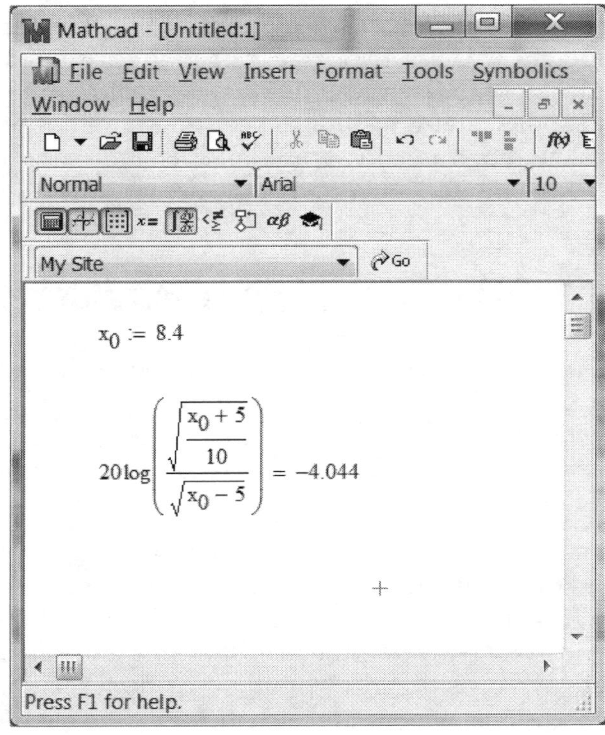

### 3.1.3 All Those Equal Signs!

Here is quick review of the five (5!) different equal signs in Mathcad

- := (colon equal) this is the assignment operator for variables or the operator to define a function.
- = (non-bold equal) evaluates an expression, i.e., calculator output.
- **=** (bold equal: cntl+=) creates a Boolean expression, such as the one needed for the "Given-Find" function. This is also handy for creating an equation as a figure in a text portion. No calculation operation is attempted and no error is given.
- ≡ (priority equal: type ~) this is used instead of the := to define a variable anywhere on the sheet. The read order of right-down is ignored, and equations with priority equal variables are evaluated first.
- → (symbolic equal: cntl+period) this is used instead of the evaluation equal when a symbolic equation needs to be calculated, such as an indefinite integral.

The Mathcad examples are

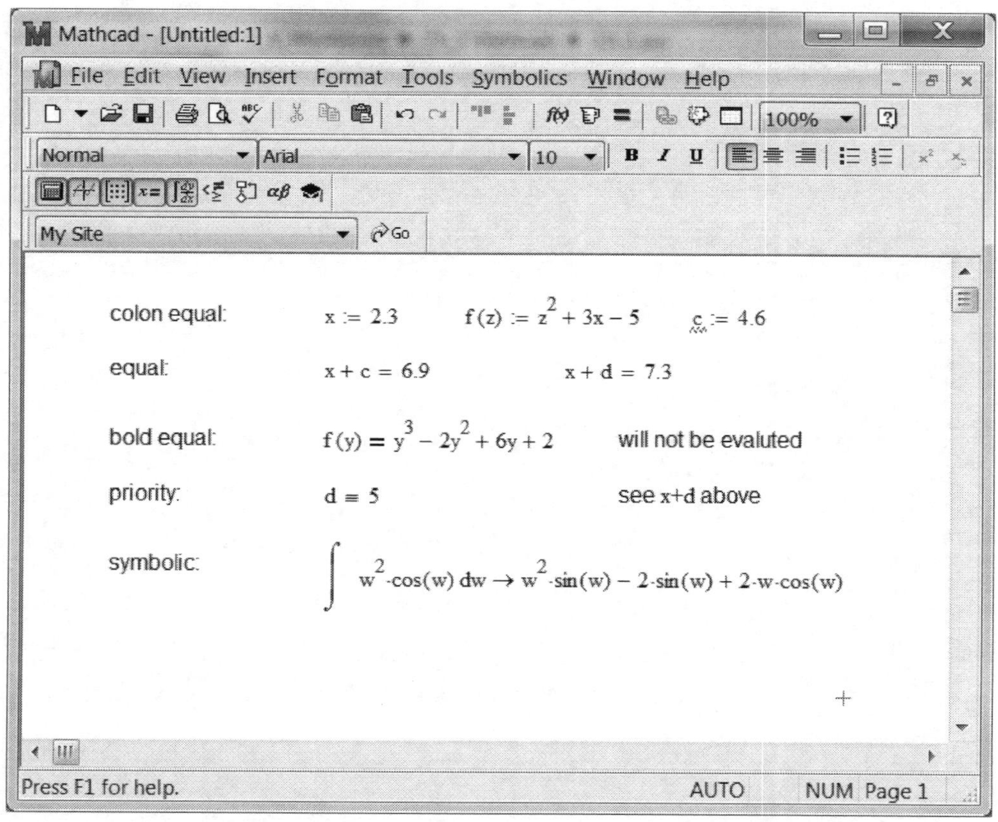

## 3.1.4 Units and Predefined Variables

One of the strongest features of Mathcad is the ability to handle units and convert units. Units from different systems can be mixed in equations and calculations performed with output in the desired systems and consistency is maintained. The user can also modify or change systems in a particular expression as desired. Unit expressions and built-in defined units are viewed at **Tools | Worksheet Options | Unit System**.

Mathcad also has a number of predefined variables built in, such as gravity (*g*) and speed of light (*c*). They are too numerous to mention here, but the list can be found in the Help Menu under **Reference Tables**. As in other programming tools, it is possible to redefine a built-in variable. This is potentially dangerous, as once this is done, the original value is lost in that worksheet. Mathcad warns the user when this has been done by underlining the new variable definition with a green squiggly line as shown. Here are a few examples:

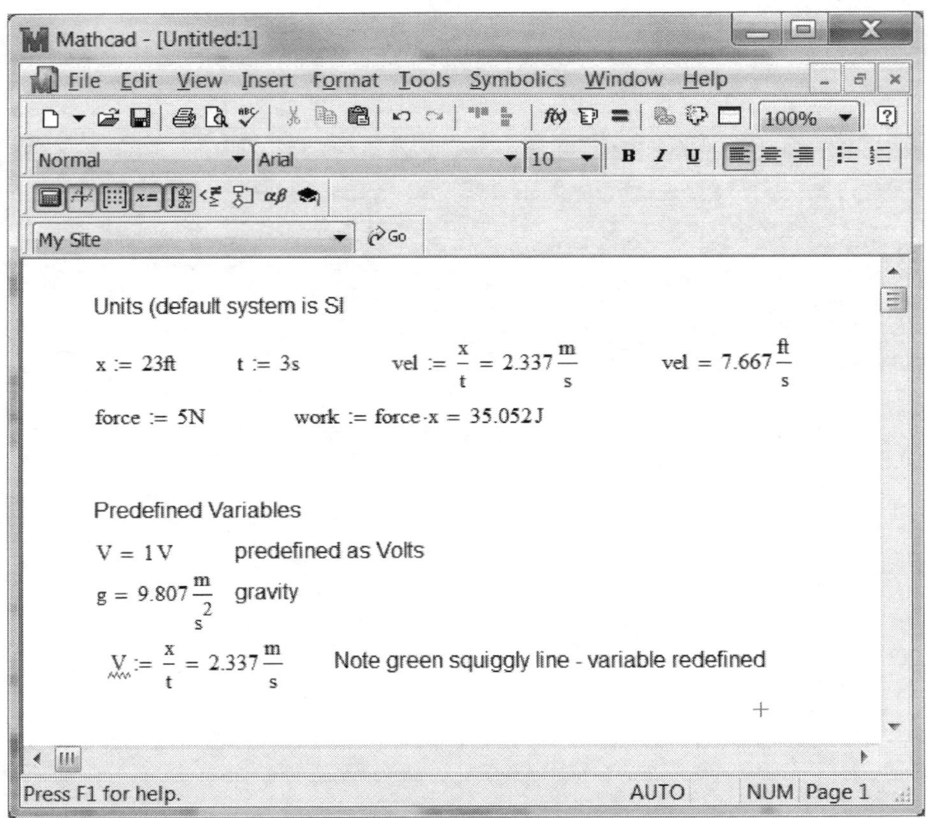

# 3.2 MATHCAD WORKED EXAMPLES

## 3.2.1 Matrices and Matrix Algebra

Open the Matrix Toolbar.

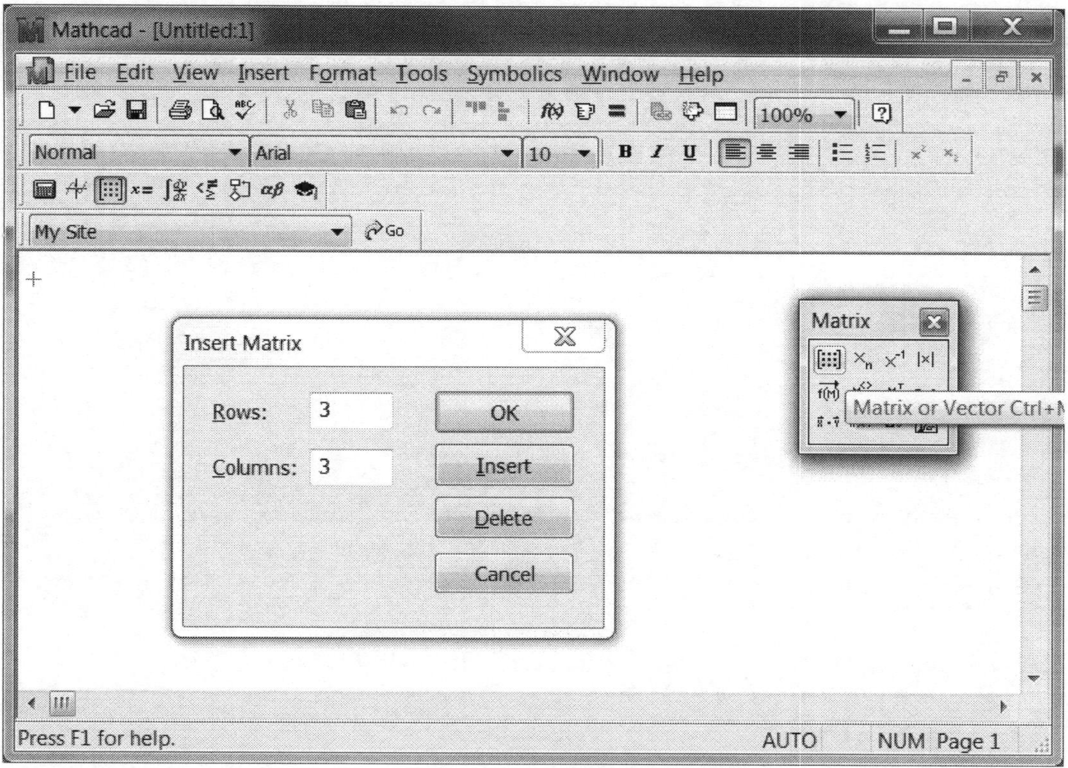


### Example 3.2.1-1

Create the following arrays using the Matrix Toolbar.

a. Create the row vector $\mathbf{a} = [2 \quad 3 \quad 4]$

b. Create the column vector

$$\mathbf{b} = \begin{bmatrix} 5 \\ 3 \\ 1 \end{bmatrix}$$

c. Create the 2x3 matrix

$$\mathbf{c} = \begin{bmatrix} 1 & 2 & 3 \\ 4 & 5 & 6 \end{bmatrix}$$

d. Create the 3x3 matrix

$$\mathbf{mata} = \begin{bmatrix} -1 & 2 & 0 \\ 7 & 3 & 1 \\ 2 & 4 & -2 \end{bmatrix}$$

The Mathcad session is

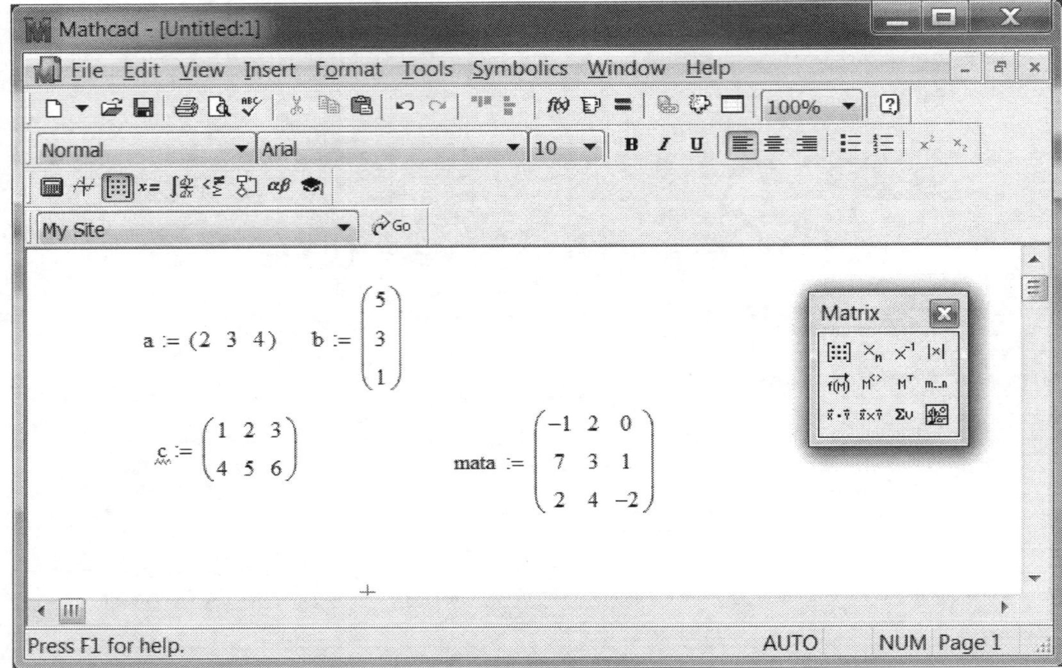


## Example 3.2.1-2

This will be an example of array addressing and ORIGIN using Example 3.2.1-1:

a. Create $\mathbf{d} = \begin{bmatrix} -1 & 2 & 0 \\ 7 & 3 & 1 \\ 2 & 4 & -2 \\ 4 & 5 & 6 \end{bmatrix}$ from *mata* and row 2 of **c**.

b. Create $\mathbf{e} = \begin{bmatrix} 2 & 4 \\ 4 & 5 \end{bmatrix}$ from *d*.

c. Create $\mathbf{f} = [2 \quad 3]$ from *c*.

The Mathcad session is

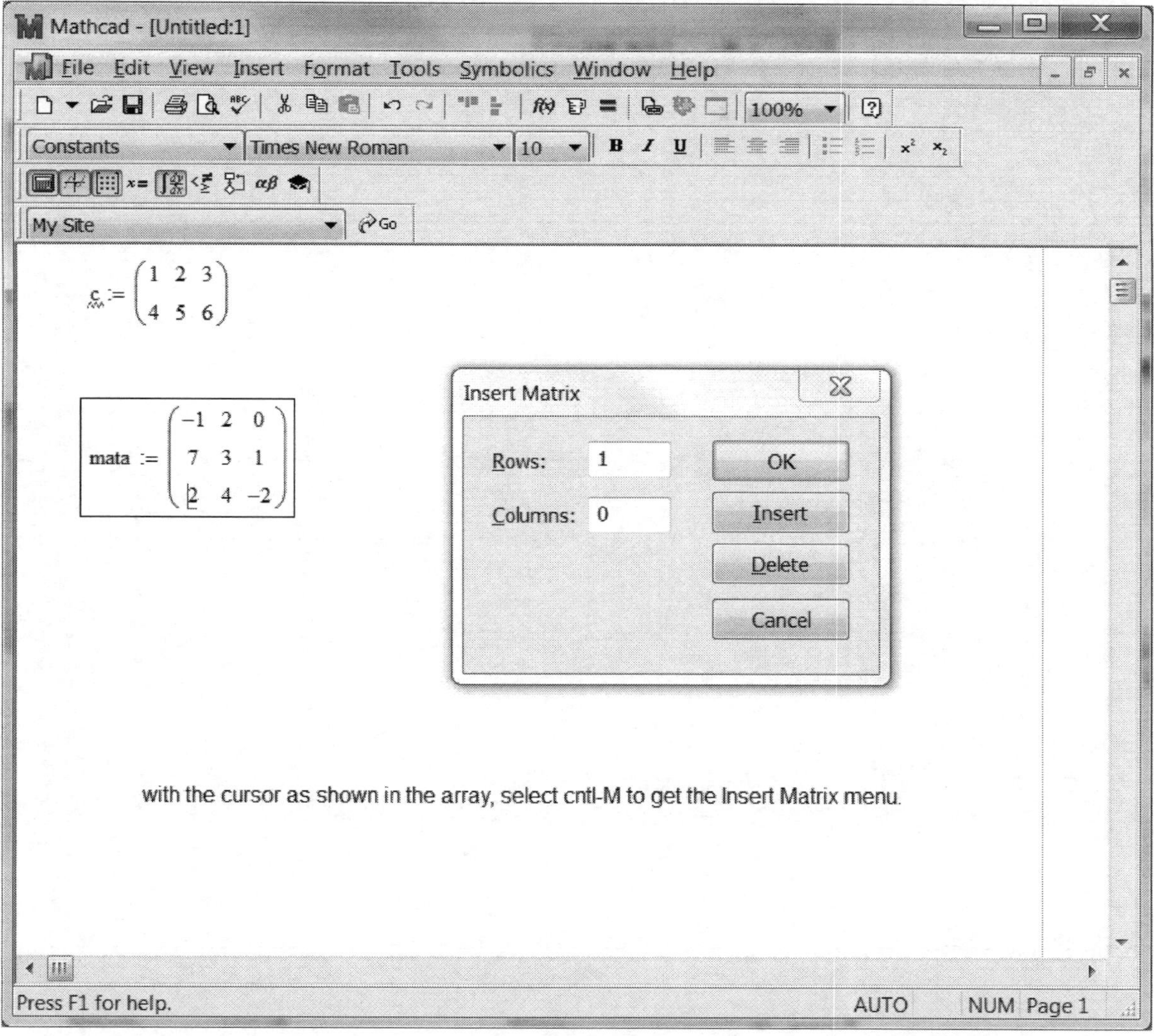

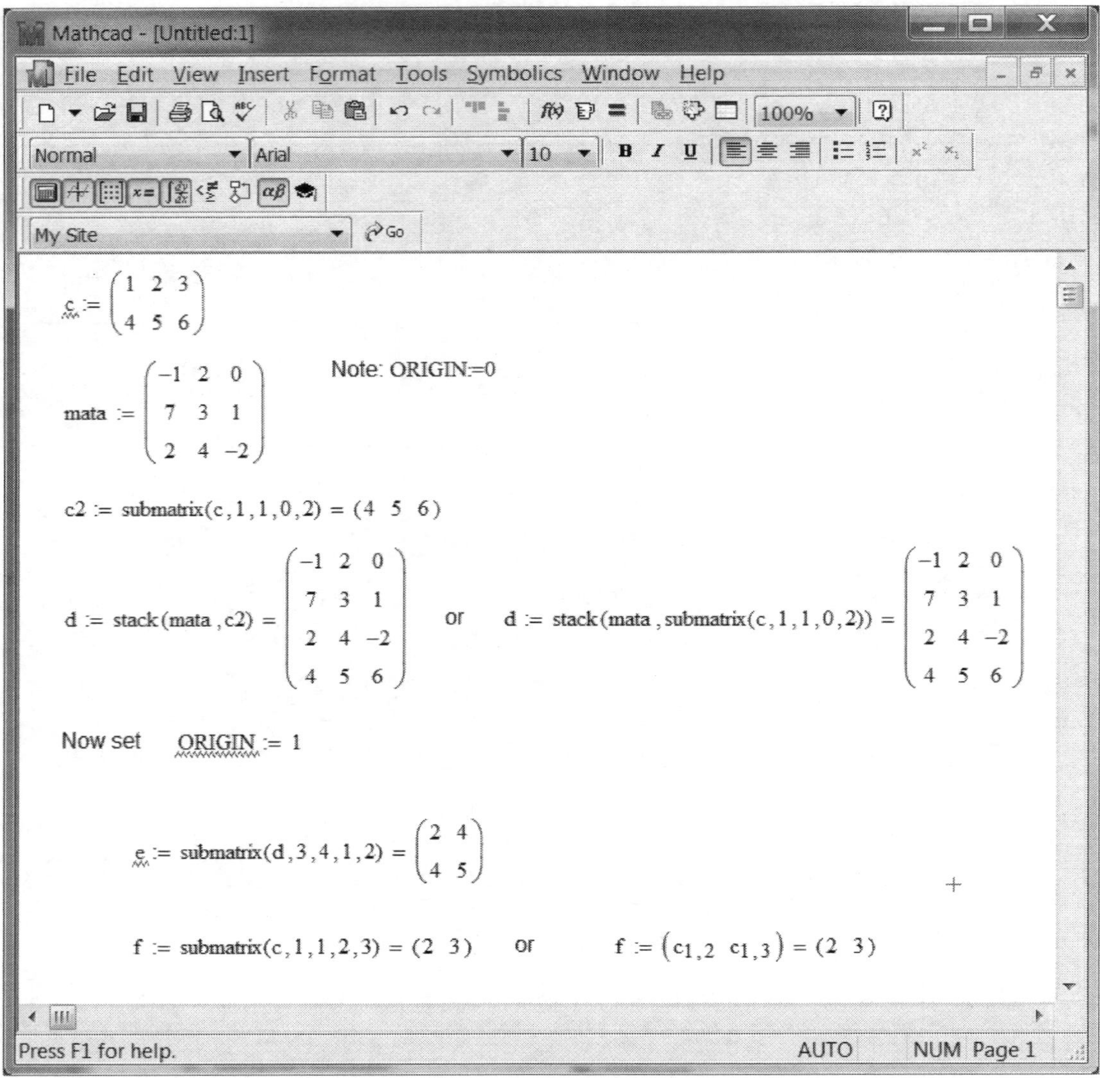


## Example 3.2.1-3 Matrix math

Using the previously created matrices **a, b,** and **mata**:

a. Multiply **a*b**
b. Multiply **b*a**
c. Multiply **a*mata**
d. Multiply **mata*b** (Note that **b*mata** results in an error)
e. Add **a+b**$^T$ (note the transpose operator on the toolbat)
f. Find the determinant of mata (use the toolbar operator. note that the absolute value operator on the Calculator tool bar can also be used as that determinant operator, but not the opposite)
g. Find the inverse of **mata**

The Mathcad session is

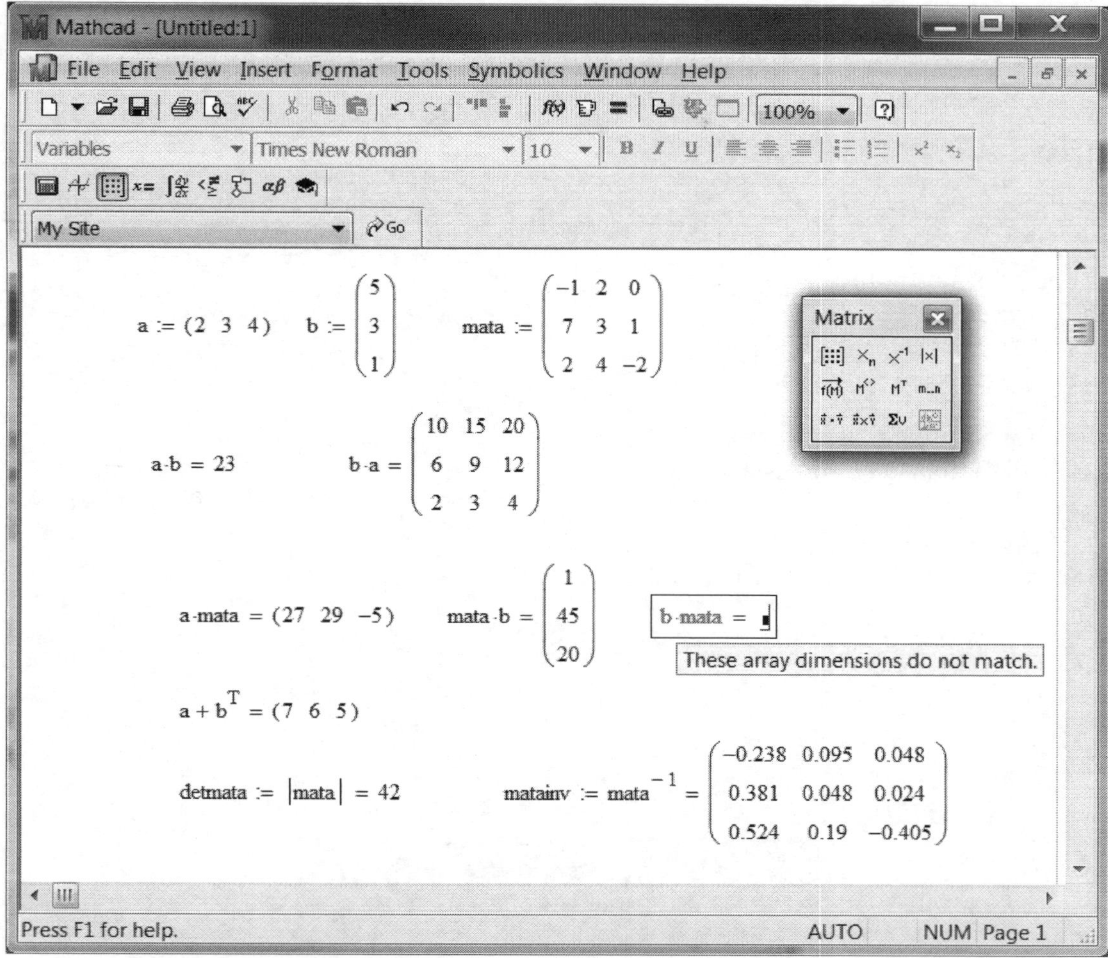


## 3.2.2 Complex Numbers in Mathcad

The imaginary number $i, j = \sqrt{-1}$ is included in Mathcad's predefined variables. Complex numbers can be entered using these predefined variables without multiplication operators (Figure 3.2.1).

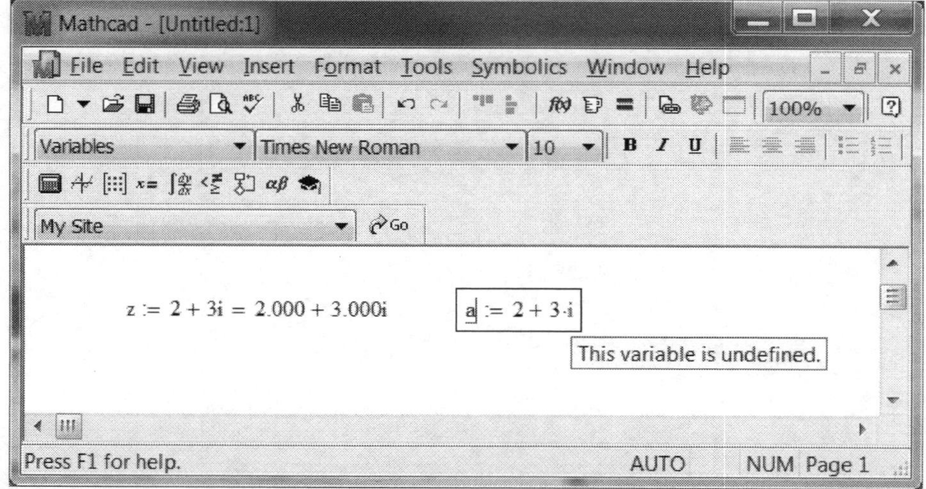


**Figure 3.2.1**

Note that Mathcad will only display one format (the rectangular format), but the standard complex number functions are available as demonstrated below. CAUTION: It is possible to redefine the value of ***i*** (or *j*) and produce unexpected results depending on how the equation is typed. Observe the different results in these two expressions for *z* (Figure 3.2.2).

i := 2.5

z := 2 + 3i = 2.000 + 3.000i

a := 2 + 3·i = 9.500

Figure 3.2.2

## Example 3.2.2-1

Given $zz = 1.9\,e^{(3.5-0.3i)} + (2-5i)$, Find:

a. *zz* in Rectangular (Standard) Form
b. (angle), arg(*zz*)
c. Re(*zz*)
d. Im(*zz*)
e. mod(*zz*) (absolute value operator on the Calculator Toolbar recognizes a complex argument)
f. conj(*zz*) (the conjugate operator is the ["] if typed immediately after the complex variable

The Mathcad session is

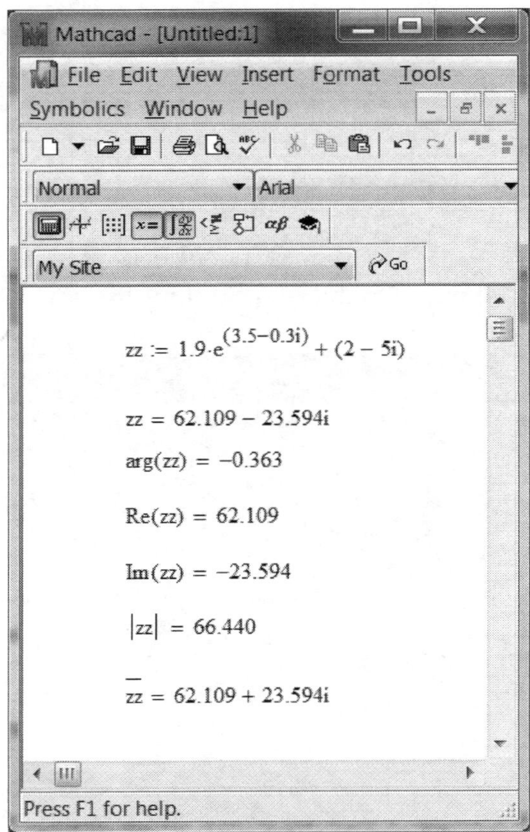

## Example 3.2.2-2

Find all the roots of $z^4 - 4iz = 0$ using the **root** function.

This function finds the roots of polynomials where x is a vector of the coefficients. The first element of the vector must be the coefficient of the highest order term and zero placeholders must be included for any missing terms. The last element will be the constant term, if any. The polynomial shown above illustrates this requirement:

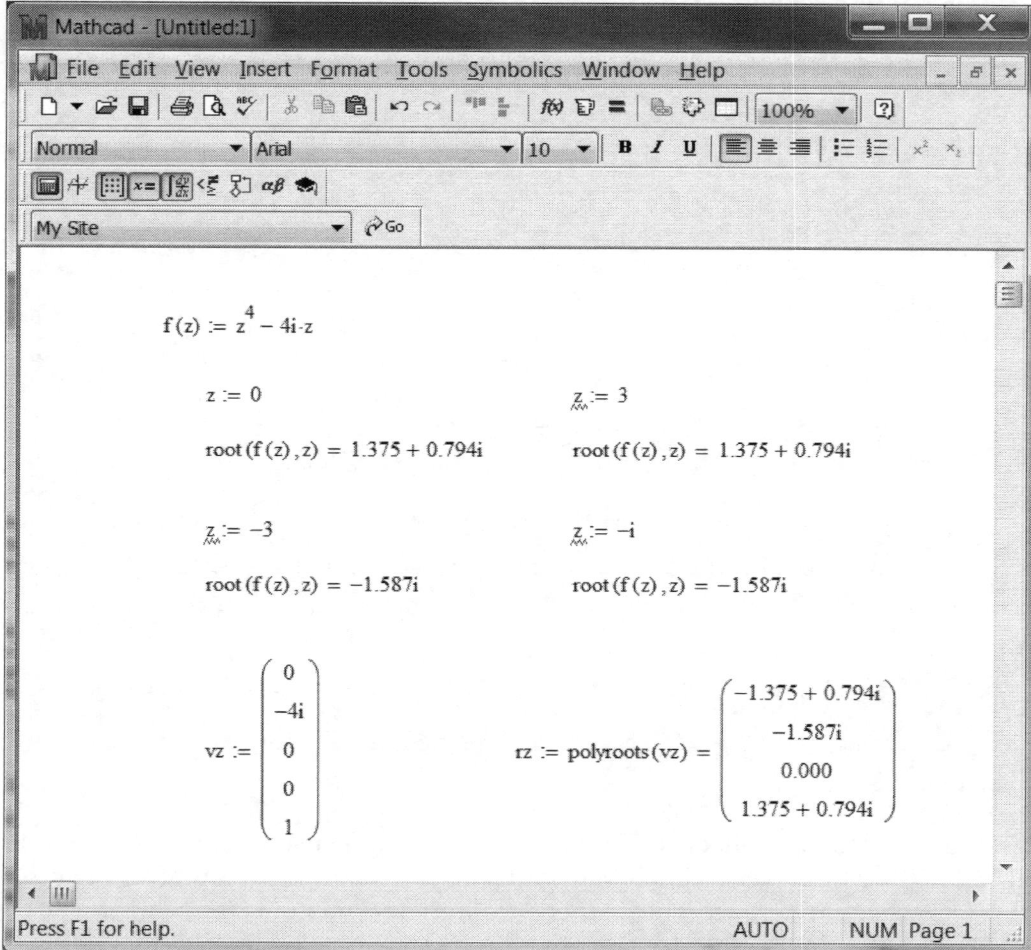


The root function in Mathcad requires a "guess". Notice that the expression is the same for all four roots, only the guess is changed to identify the specific root. It helps if a graph of the function is available, to zero in on the correct root.

### 3.2.3 Using Mathcad Worksheet Solutions as Functions

Figure 3.2.3 shows how to use simple functions in a worksheet.

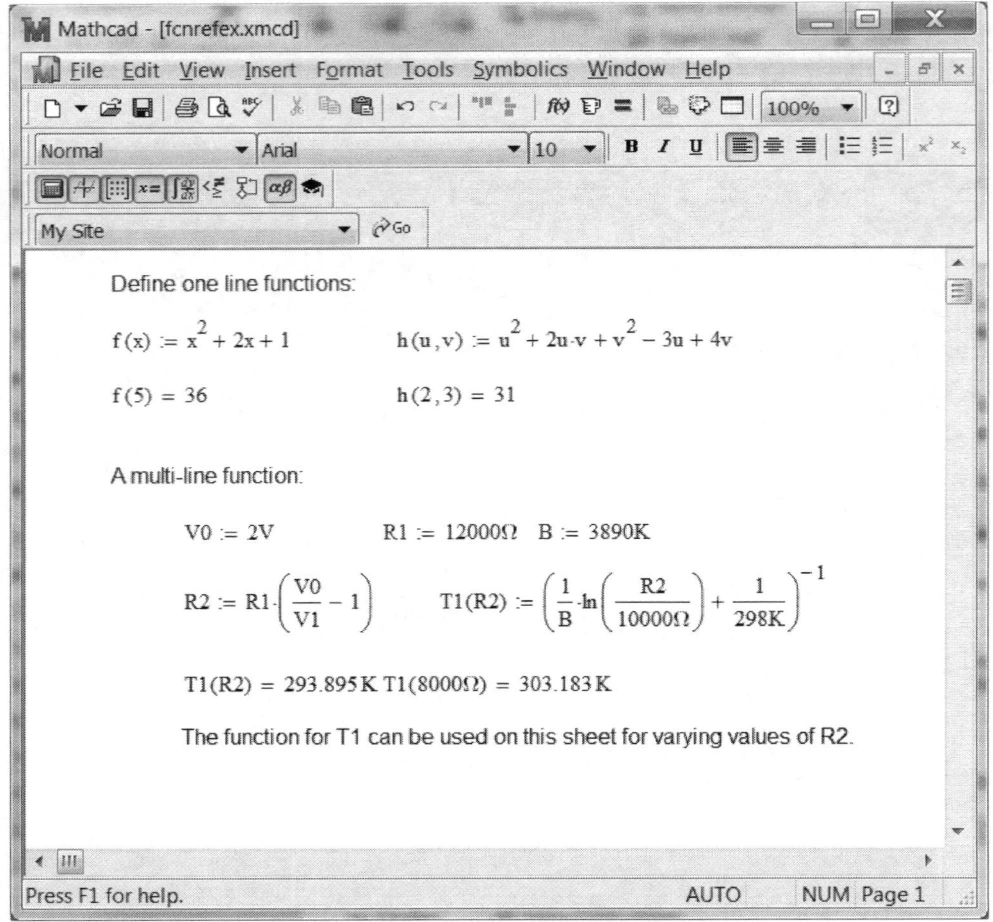


**Figure 3.2.3**

In many cases, a detailed worksheet calculation may need to be used many times. Just like a function call in MATLAB or the TI-89, a saved Mathcad worksheet can be "referenced" externally. In this example, the worksheet "reference_sheet.xmcd" defines several constants and defines a function that calculates atmospheric pressure for a given altitude. The new worksheet that desires to use the function creates a link to the reference worksheet from the menu **Insert | Reference,** and specifies the filename path.

## Example 3.2.3-1

Create an external reference function in Mathcad and use the function in an external worksheet:

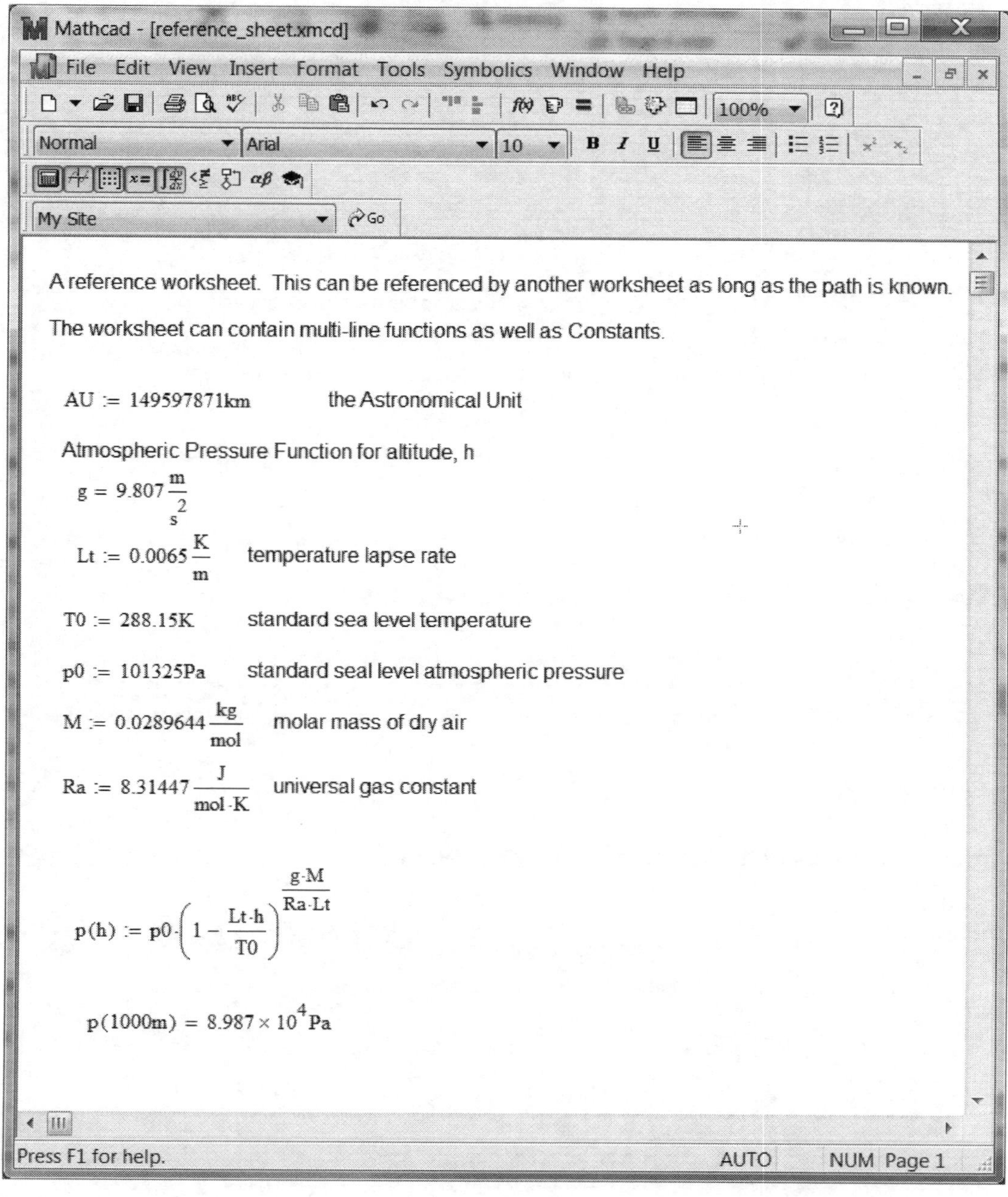

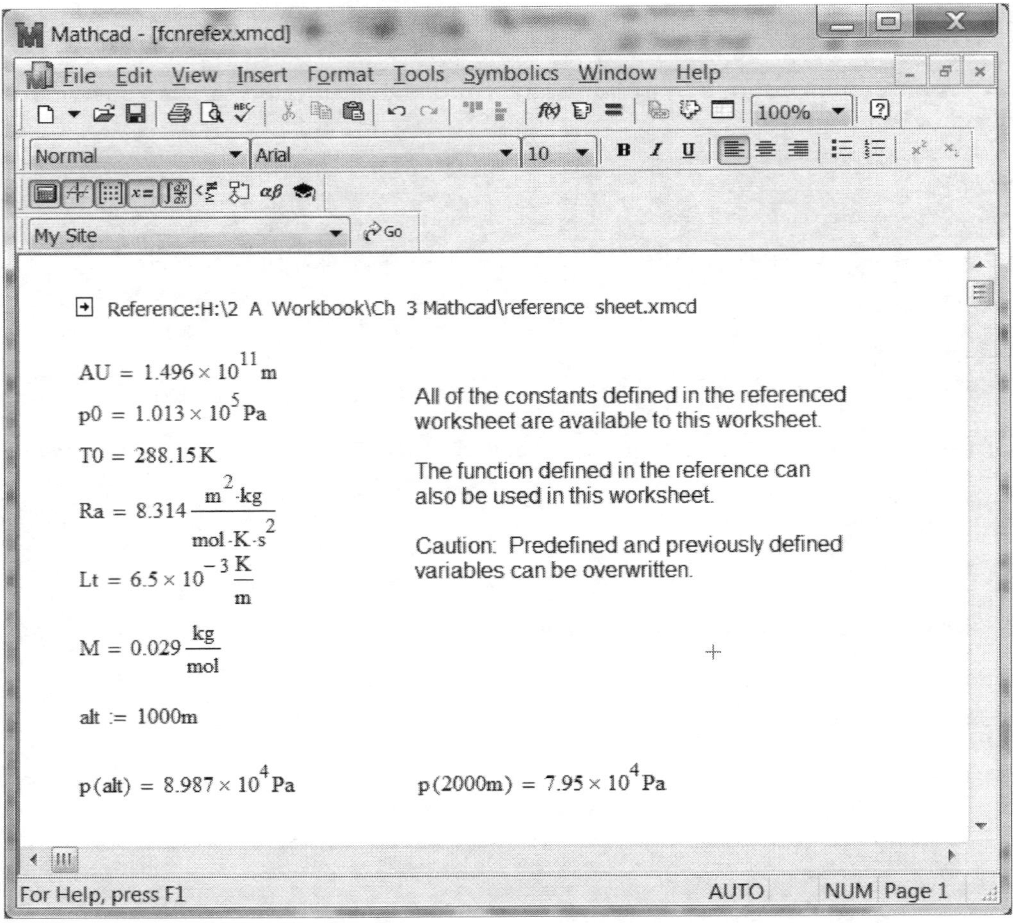


## Example 3.2.3-2

Create a function worksheet to find the volume of a sphere for any radius, where $\text{Vol} = \frac{4}{3}\pi r^3$.

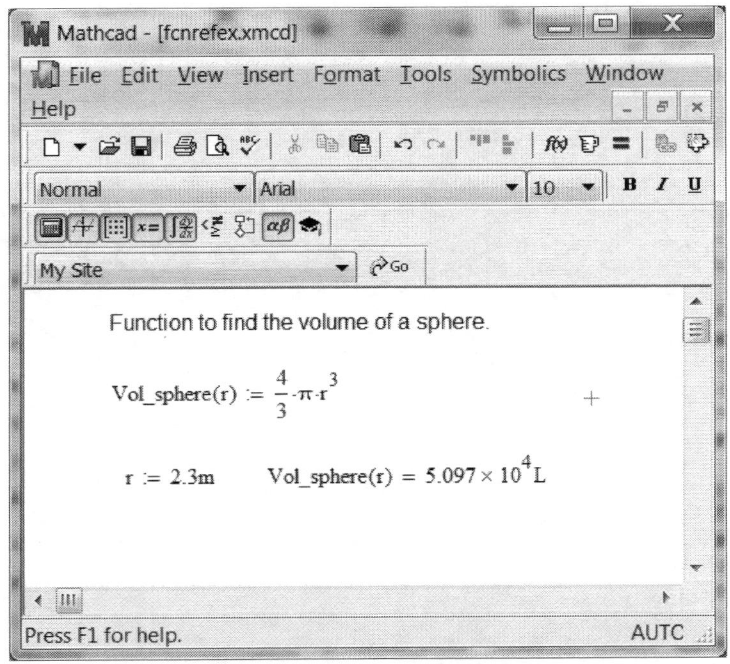

## Example 3.2.3-3

Create a worksheet in Mathcad that can be used as an external reference, similar to a function with multiple output results, as well as multiple variables for input arguments. The worksheet calculates the volume and surface area of a closed cylinder when given the height and radius. The governing equations are

$$\text{Vol}_{\text{CYL}} = \pi * r^2 * h \qquad \text{SArea}_{\text{CYL}} = (2 * \pi * r^2) + (2 * \pi * r * h)$$

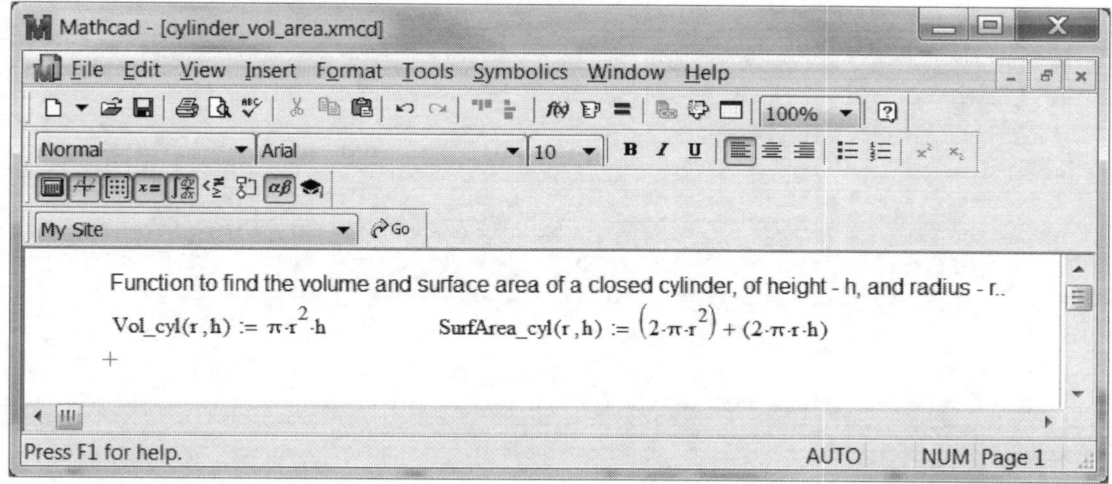


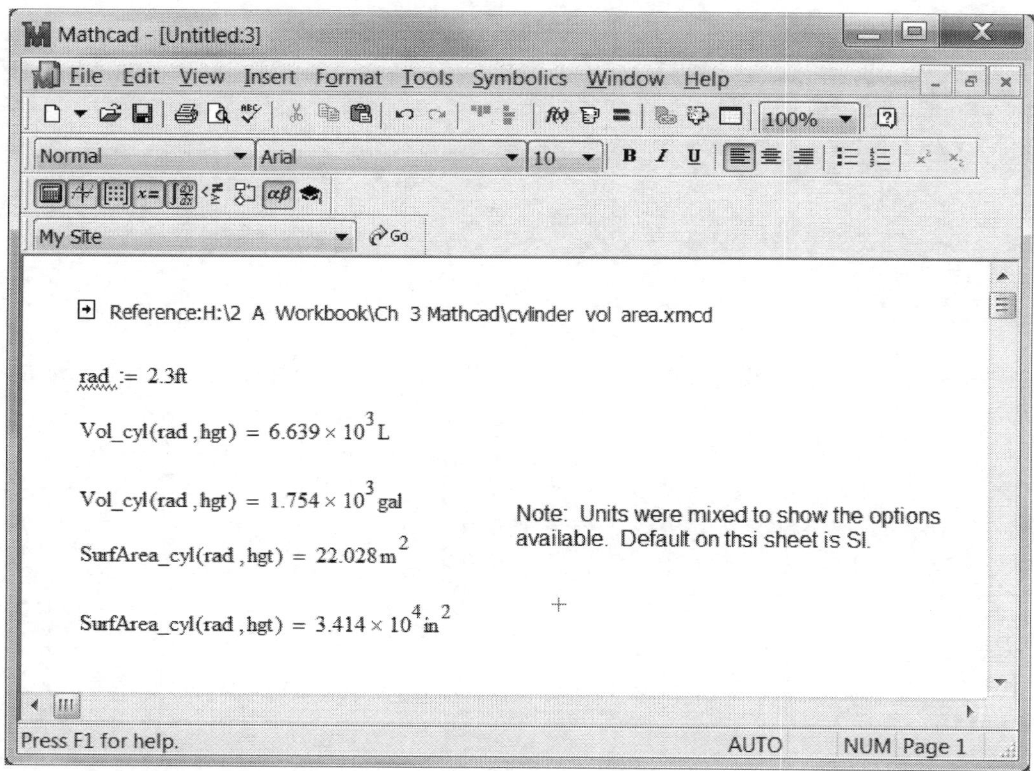

### 3.2.4 Solving Systems of Linear Equations in Mathcad

The previous examples of linear system are solved in Mathcad.

## Example 3.2.4-1

Solve the following system of equations for [*x*,*y*,*z*].

$$\begin{aligned} x-2y+3z&=2 \\ 2x+y-7z&=6 \\ x-y-z&=1 \end{aligned} \quad \text{convert to matrix form} \quad \begin{bmatrix} 1 & -2 & 3 \\ 2 & 1 & -7 \\ 1 & -1 & -1 \end{bmatrix} \begin{bmatrix} x \\ y \\ z \end{bmatrix} = \begin{bmatrix} 2 \\ 6 \\ 1 \end{bmatrix}$$

The solution is $\bar{x} = A^{-1} * \bar{\mathbf{d}}$

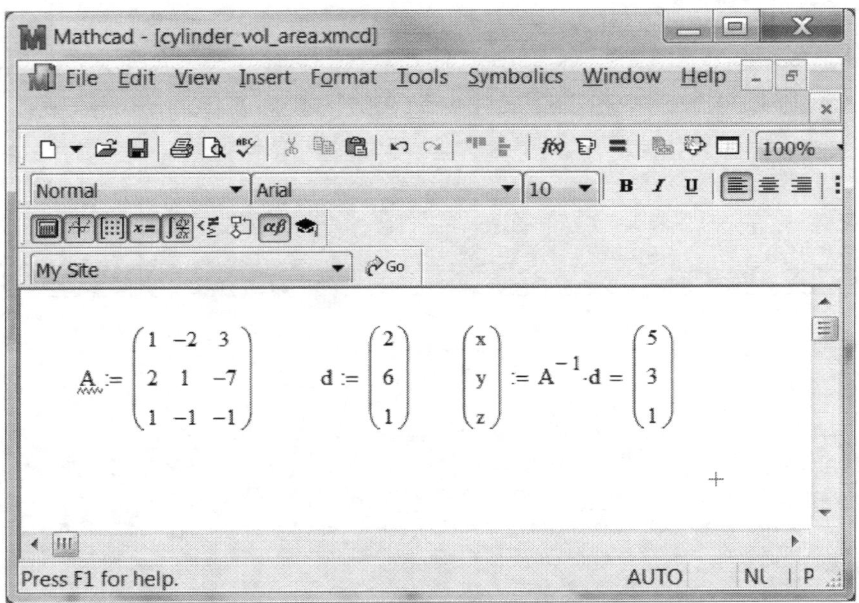


## Example 3.2.4-2

The electric circuit from Example 1.2.4-2 is solved using Mathcad. The matrix equation is

$$\begin{bmatrix} (R_1+R_2+R_3) & -R_2 & -R_3 \\ -R_2 & (R_2+R_4+R_6) & -R_6 \\ -R_3 & -R_6 & (R_3+R_5+R_6) \end{bmatrix} \begin{bmatrix} i_1 \\ i_2 \\ i_3 \end{bmatrix} = \begin{bmatrix} V_1 \\ 0 \\ 0 \end{bmatrix}$$

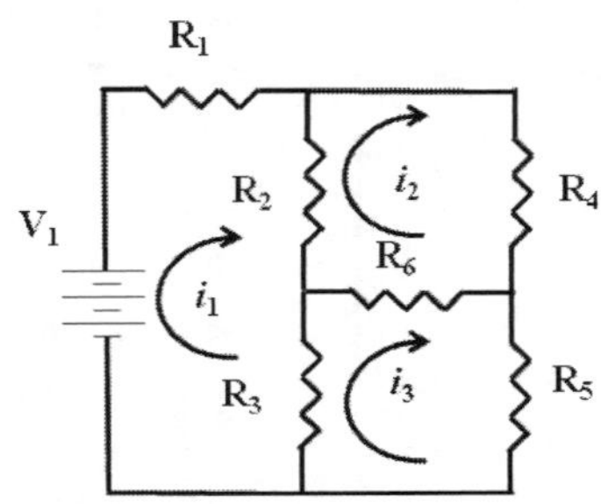


The values are

$$R_1 = 5\Omega \quad R_2 = 15\Omega \quad R_3 = 8\Omega \quad R_4 = 10\Omega \quad R_5 = 7\Omega \quad R_6 = 12\Omega \quad V_1 = 9V$$

And then substituting for the given values of $R$'s and $V_1$, the Mathcad session is

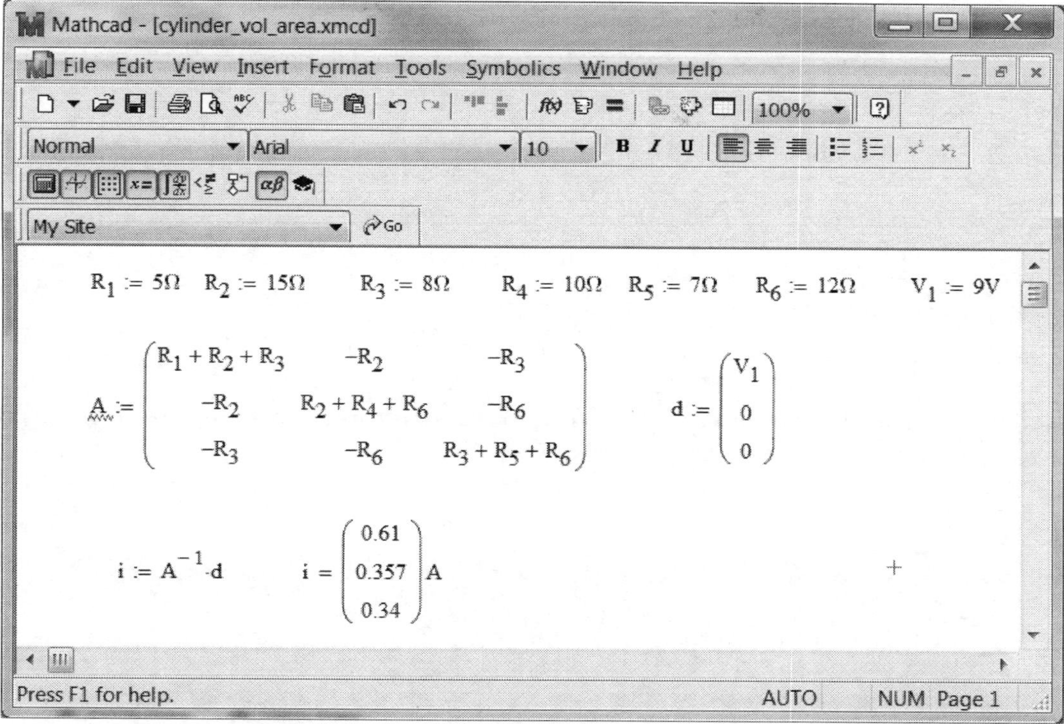

## Example 3.2.4-3 Solving systems of linear equations by Gaussian elimination.

Mathcad also has only the `rref(augmat)` function to produce the Reduced Row Echelon Form from the augmented matrix of linear equations. This is convenient because the resulting matrix displays the solution directly. Recall that the augmented matrix is created by appending the $\overline{\mathbf{d}}$ vector to the coefficient matrix $A$. Using the equations from Example 3.2.4-1, the Mathcad session to create the augmented matrix and the `rref()` solution is

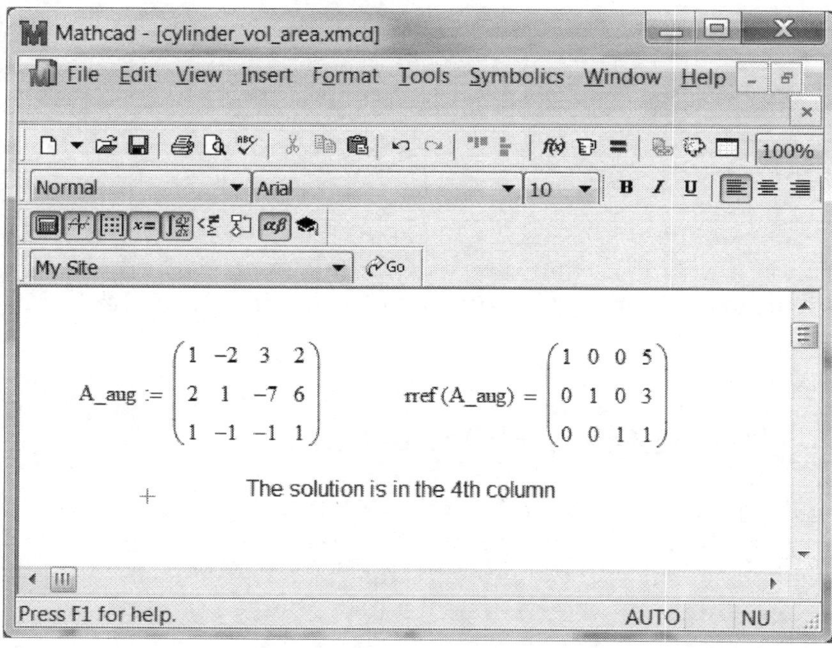

## Example 3.2.4-4 An Infinite Solution system.

Again, consider the following system of linear equations:

$$\begin{aligned} x+y-z&=1 \\ 3x-y+3z&=5 \\ x-y+2z&=2 \end{aligned} \quad \text{The matrix equation is} \quad \begin{bmatrix} 1 & 1 & -1 \\ 3 & -1 & 3 \\ 1 & -1 & 2 \end{bmatrix}\begin{bmatrix} x \\ y \\ z \end{bmatrix} = \begin{bmatrix} 1 \\ 5 \\ 2 \end{bmatrix}$$

And the augmented matrix is $$\begin{bmatrix} A & b \end{bmatrix} = \begin{bmatrix} 1 & 1 & -1 & 1 \\ 3 & -1 & 3 & 5 \\ 1 & -1 & 2 & 2 \end{bmatrix}$$

Note that det($A$) = 0, and so the inverse does not exist; therefore, a unique solution does not exist. Gaussian elimination reveals the following result:

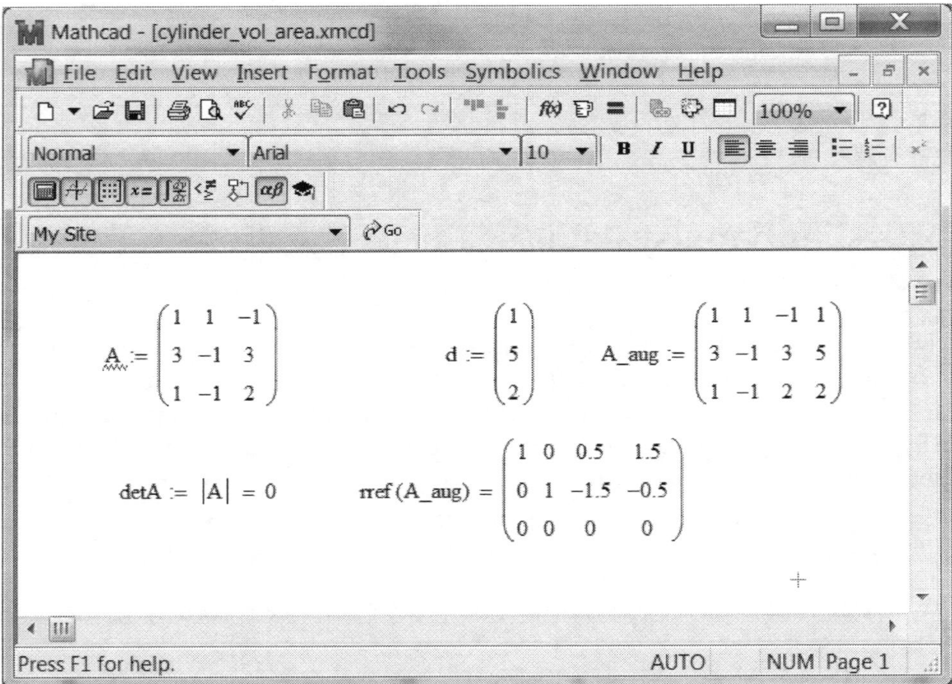


The Infinite Solution is the same as that discussed in this example in the MATLAB chapter. This gives a result as to which is the parametric equation of a straight-line in three dimensions, as shown in Example 2.2.4-4.

## Example 3.2.4-5. Using the *rank()* function.

Using the system of linear equations from Example 3.2.4-1: As the determinant is not 0, and the rank of the coefficient matrix $A$ is equal to the number of unknowns ($n$ = 3), matrix $A$ represents three independent equations. The rank of the augmented matrix is also equal to the number of unknowns. Meeting these three conditions indicates a system with a unique solution.

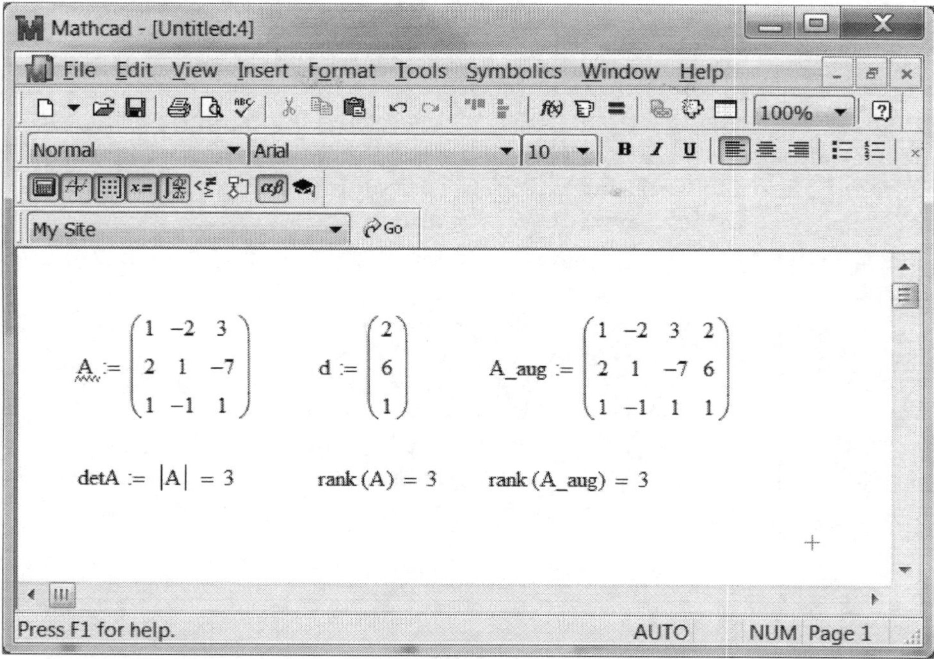


Compare this result to the system of Example 3.2.4-1

For Example 3.2.4-4, as the determinant is 0, a unique solution does not exist. The Mathcad solution is shown, as *rank(A) = rank([AAUG])*, an Infinite Solution exists, represented by a straight-line in three dimensions. The Mathcad equivalent of the MATLAB pseudoinverse function (`pinv`) is called **geninv**(), and the solution is shown in the following figure. This solution is a unique point in the 3D Cartesian system that is the point of closest approach to the origin of the infinite line solution. See the figure in Example 2.2.4-4

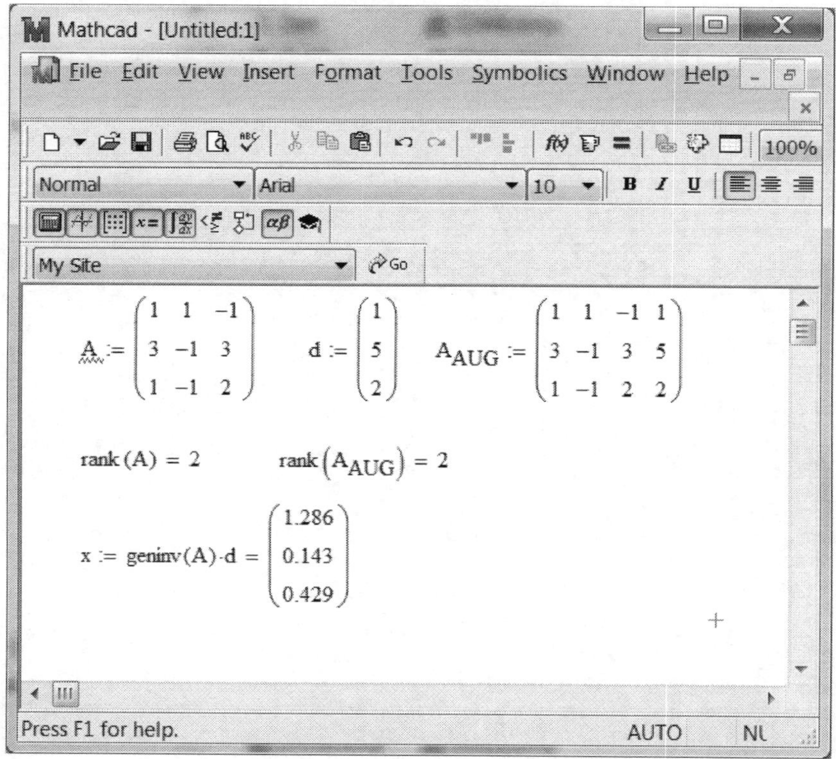

## Example 3.2.4-6

Given the truss system with the loadings in the following figure, solve for the 11 unknown forces and the three unknown external reactions. Since there are seven pin joints, the theory of truss analysis can generate 14 independent equations to solve for the 14 unknowns. Find the solution using both the matrix inverse and the Gaussian elimination methods.

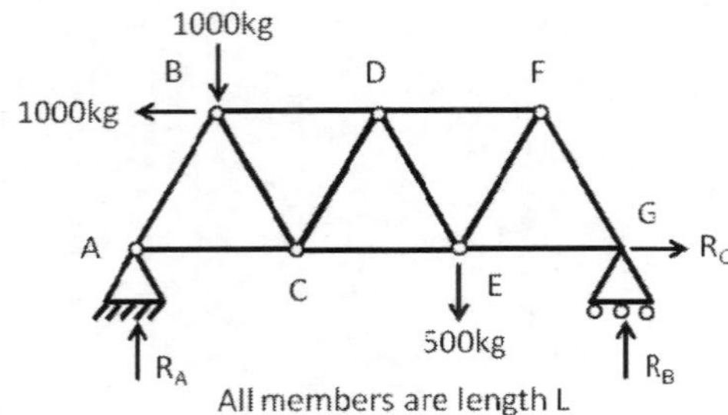


The equations are:

$$R_A + T_{AB}\sin\theta = 0$$
$$T_{AB}\cos\theta + T_{AC} = 0$$
$$-T_{AB}\sin\theta - T_{BC}\sin\theta - 1000 = 0$$
$$-T_{AB}\cos\theta + T_{BC}\cos\theta + T_{BD} - 1000 = 0$$
$$T_{BC}\sin\theta + T_{CD}\sin\theta = 0$$
$$-T_{AC} - T_{BC}\cos\theta + T_{CD}\cos\theta + T_{CE} = 0$$
$$-T_{DC}\sin\theta - T_{DE}\sin\theta = 0$$
$$-T_{BD} - T_{CD}\cos\theta + T_{DE}\cos\theta + T_{DF} = 0$$
$$T_{ED}\sin\theta + T_{EF}\sin\theta - 500 = 0$$
$$-T_{EC} - T_{ED}\cos\theta + T_{EF}\cos\theta + T_{AB} = 0$$
$$-T_{EF}\sin\theta - T_{FG}\sin\theta = 0$$
$$-T_{DF} - T_{EF}\cos\theta + T_{FG}\cos\theta = 0$$
$$R_B - T_{FG}\sin\theta = 0$$
$$R_C - T_{EG} - T_{FG}\cos\theta = 0$$

And in matrix form:

$$\begin{bmatrix} 1 & 0 & 0 & \sin\theta & 0 & 0 & 0 & 0 & 0 & 0 & 0 & 0 & 0 & 0 \\ 0 & 0 & 0 & \cos\theta & 1 & 0 & 0 & 0 & 0 & 0 & 0 & 0 & 0 & 0 \\ 0 & 0 & 0 & -\sin\theta & -\sin\theta & 0 & 0 & 0 & 0 & 0 & 0 & 0 & 0 & 0 \\ 0 & 0 & 0 & -\cos\theta & 0 & \cos\theta & 1 & 0 & 0 & 0 & 0 & 0 & 0 & 0 \\ 0 & 0 & 0 & 0 & 0 & \sin\theta & 0 & \sin\theta & 0 & 0 & 0 & 0 & 0 & 0 \\ 0 & 0 & 0 & 0 & -1 & -\cos\theta & 0 & \cos\theta & 1 & 0 & 0 & 0 & 0 & 0 \\ 0 & 0 & 0 & 0 & 0 & 0 & 0 & 0 & -\sin\theta & 0 & -\sin\theta & 0 & 0 & 0 \\ 0 & 0 & 0 & 0 & 0 & 0 & -1 & \cos\theta & 0 & \cos\theta & 1 & 0 & 0 & 0 \\ 0 & 0 & 0 & 0 & 0 & 0 & 0 & 0 & 0 & \sin\theta & 0 & \sin\theta & 0 & 0 \\ 0 & 0 & 0 & 0 & 0 & 0 & 0 & 0 & -1 & -\cos\theta & 0 & \cos\theta & 1 & 0 \\ 0 & 0 & 0 & 0 & 0 & 0 & 0 & 0 & 0 & 0 & 0 & -1 & 0 & -1 \\ 0 & 0 & 0 & 0 & 0 & 0 & 0 & 0 & 0 & 0 & -1 & \cos\theta & 0 & \cos\theta \\ 0 & 1 & 0 & 0 & 0 & 0 & 0 & 0 & 0 & 0 & 0 & 0 & 0 & \sin\theta \\ 0 & 0 & 1 & 0 & 0 & 0 & 0 & 0 & 0 & 0 & 0 & 0 & -1 & -\cos\theta \end{bmatrix} \begin{bmatrix} R_A \\ R_B \\ R_C \\ T_{AB} \\ T_{AC} \\ T_{BC} \\ T_{BD} \\ T_{CD} \\ T_{CE} \\ T_{DE} \\ T_{DF} \\ T_{EF} \\ T_{EG} \\ T_{FG} \end{bmatrix} = \begin{bmatrix} 0 \\ 0 \\ 1000 \\ 1000 \\ 0 \\ 0 \\ 0 \\ 0 \\ 500 \\ 0 \\ 0 \\ 0 \\ 0 \\ 0 \end{bmatrix}$$

The matrix solution is $\bar{x} = A^{-1} * \bar{\mathbf{d}}$ One of the advantages of Mathcad is the ability to select display options and presentation style. Formatting documents and presentations is simplified. This result used the options available at **Format | Result**.

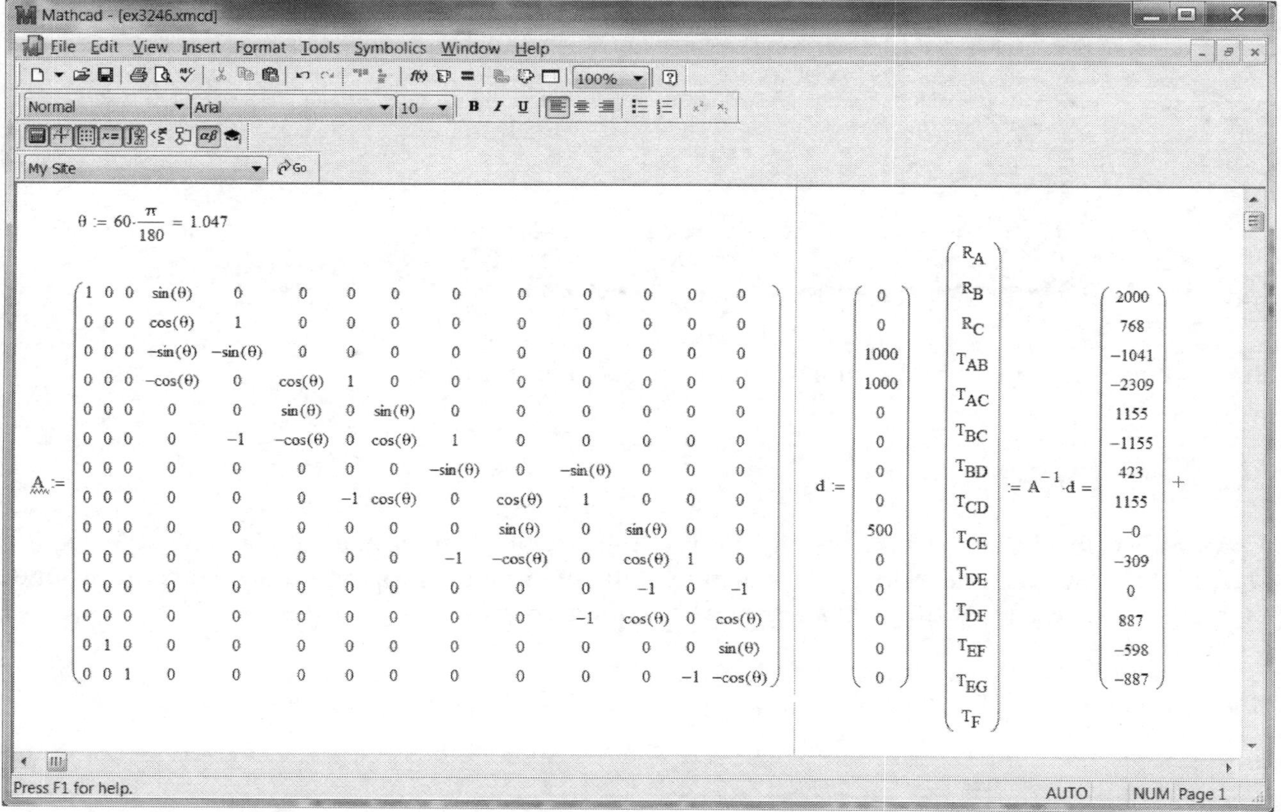

## 3.2.5 Creating Plots (Graphs) with Mathcad

Mathcad has simple menus for creating and labeling graphs, using the Graph Toolbar.

### Example 3.2.5-1

Create a graph of the $y = \exp(-0.5 * x) * \sin(x)$ function, from 0 to 2, and label the $x$ and $y$ axes.

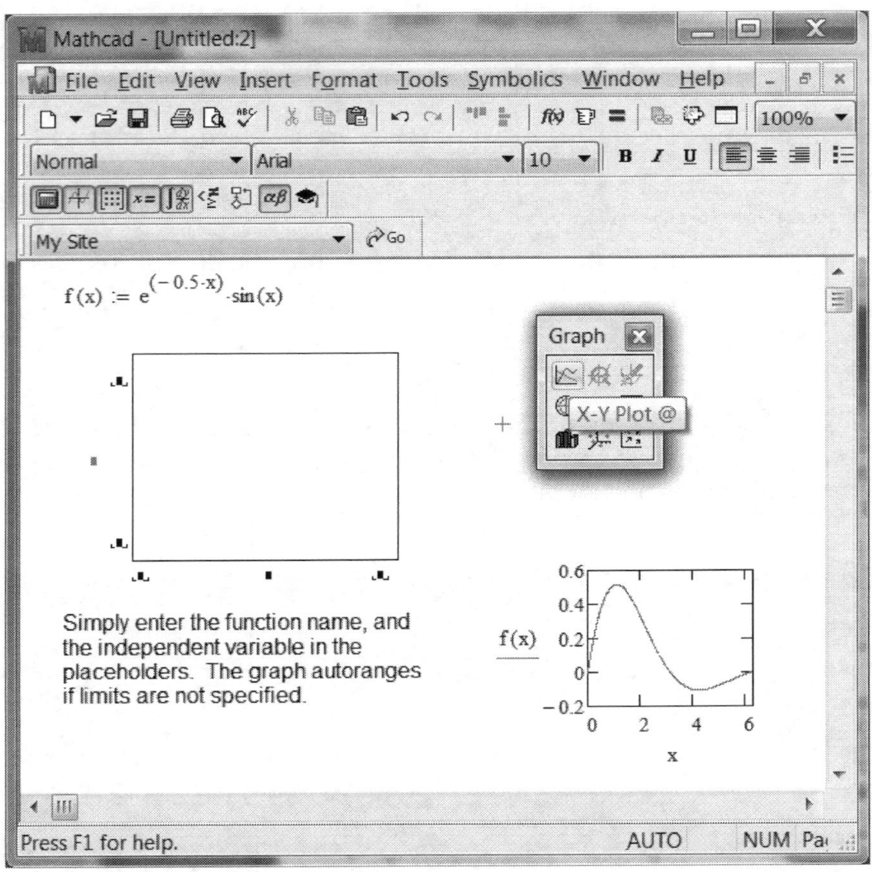


Hint: Do not forget that trig functions require angles to be in radians.

### Example 3.2.5-2

A projectile is fired from a cannon with an initial velocity of 120 m/s, at an angle of 33°. Neglecting drag, plot the altitude and velocity versus time of the flight of the projectile until it hits the ground. Label the axes, and add a title and a legend. The equations are:

$$v0y = v0 * \sin\alpha - g * t \qquad v0x = v0 * \cos\alpha \qquad h = v0 * \sin\alpha * t - 0.5 * g * t^2$$

$$time\ of\ flight = \frac{v0 * \sin\alpha}{0.5 * g} \qquad v = \sqrt{v0x^2 + v0y^2}$$

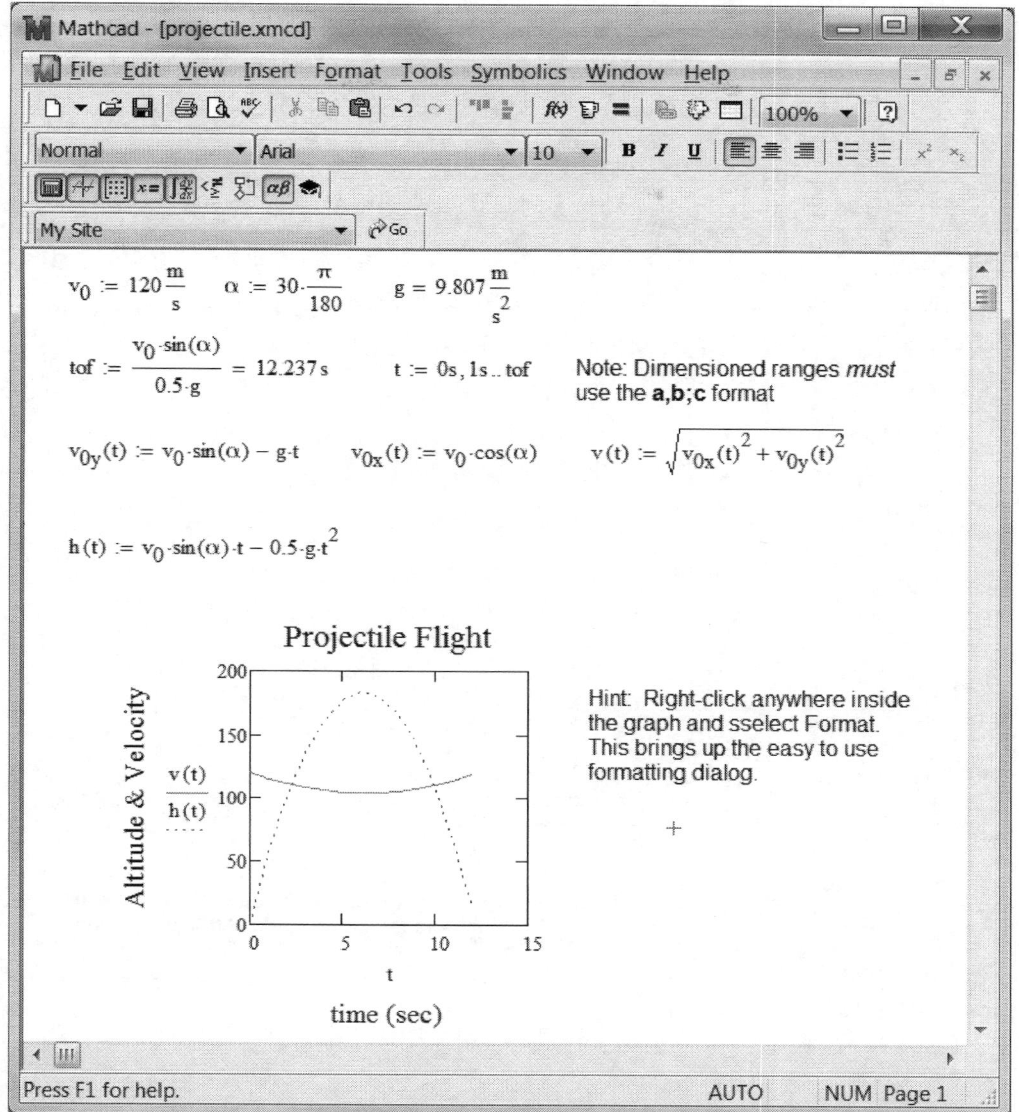

Mathcad - [projectile.xmcd]
File Edit View Insert Format Tools Symbolics Window Help
100%
Normal
Arial
10
My Site
Go
v0 := 120 m/s
α := 30·π/180
g = 9.807 m/s2
tof := v0·sin(α)/(0.5·g) = 12.237 s
t := 0s, 1s .. tof
Note: Dimensioned ranges must use the a,b;c format
v0y(t) := v0·sin(α) − g·t
v0x(t) := v0·cos(α)
v(t) := √(v0x(t)2 + v0y(t)2)
h(t) := v0·sin(α)·t − 0.5·g·t2
Projectile Flight
Altitude & Velocity
v(t)
h(t)
time (sec)
t
Hint: Right-click anywhere inside the graph and sselect Format. This brings up the easy to use formatting dialog.
Press F1 for help.
AUTO
NUM Page 1

## Example 3.2.5-3 Linear regression.

Mathcad simplifies linear regression analysis. While MATLAB, TI-89, and Excel all have linear or polynomial regression functions as well, the technique is shown here to demonstrate the solution with Mathcad graphing techniques. Given a set of x,y pairs that represent linear data, determine the slope and y-intercept of the best fit equation of the line $y = mx + b$. Plot the data points and the line on the same plot.

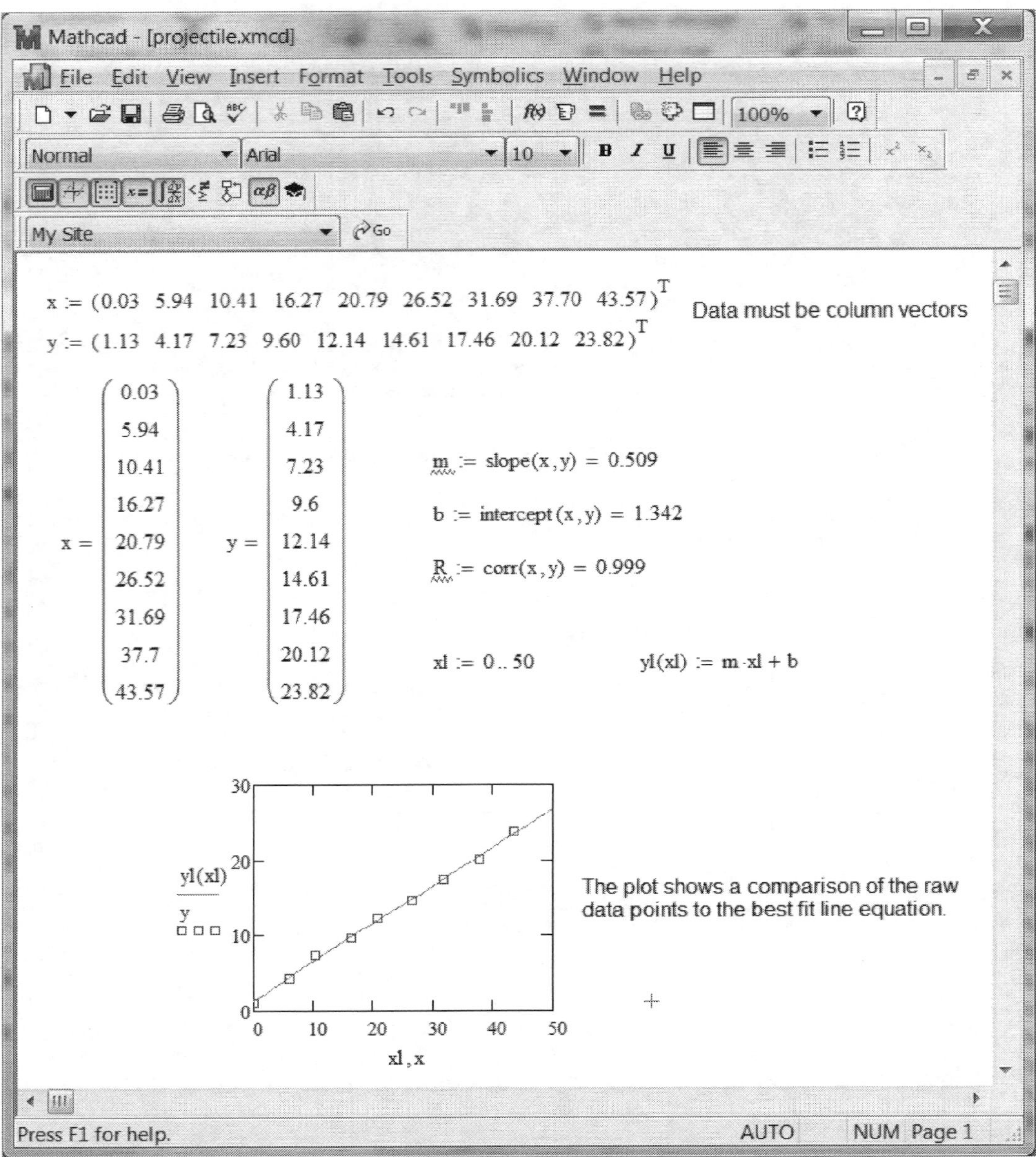


## 3.2.6 Importing Data from Sources Outside Mathcad

There are several options for importing external data into Mathcad. The **Insert | Data** menu provides choices including an **Import Data Wizard**. External data files can be defined and referenced and assigned to Mathcad variables. Import can also be accomplished using drag and drop, or copy/paste methods.

### Example 3.2.6-1

The menu **Insert | Data | File Input** allows the selection of external data files that can be assigned to variables. The file data1.txt (the following first figure) from a previous example is used again. The value of this method is that if data is changed in the external file, those changes will be reflected in new results when the Mathcad worksheet is re-executed.

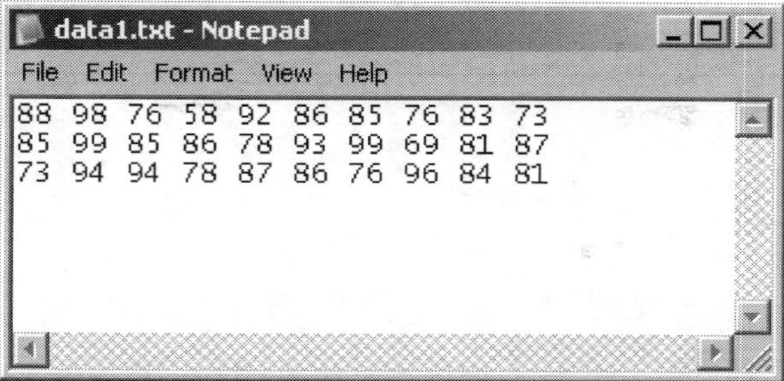


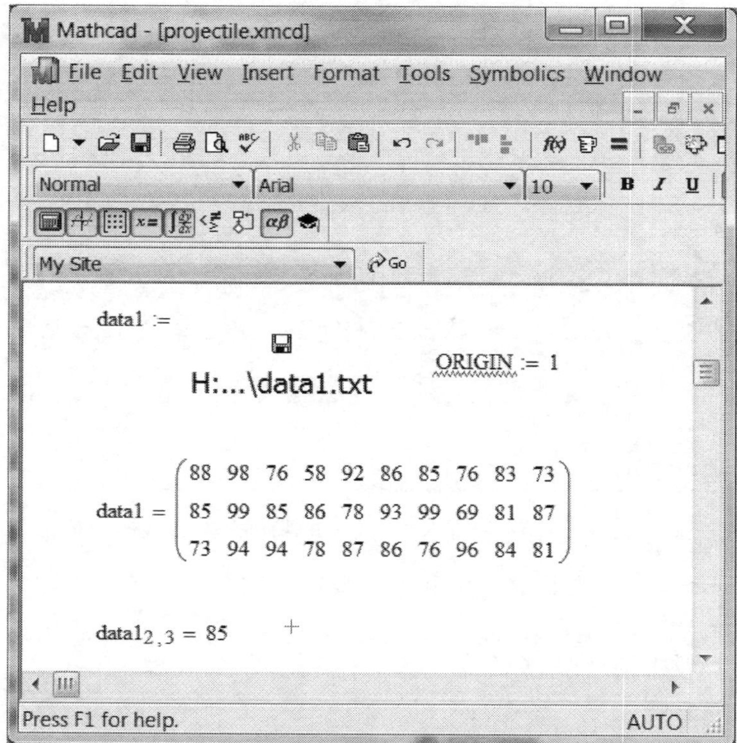


## Example 3.2.6-2

Import the data contained in an Excel file (`.xlsx`) using the copy/paste method. This is the simplest import method. However, it does not maintain a reference to the Excel worksheet. If the worksheet is changed, these changes are not reflected on the Mathcad worksheet.

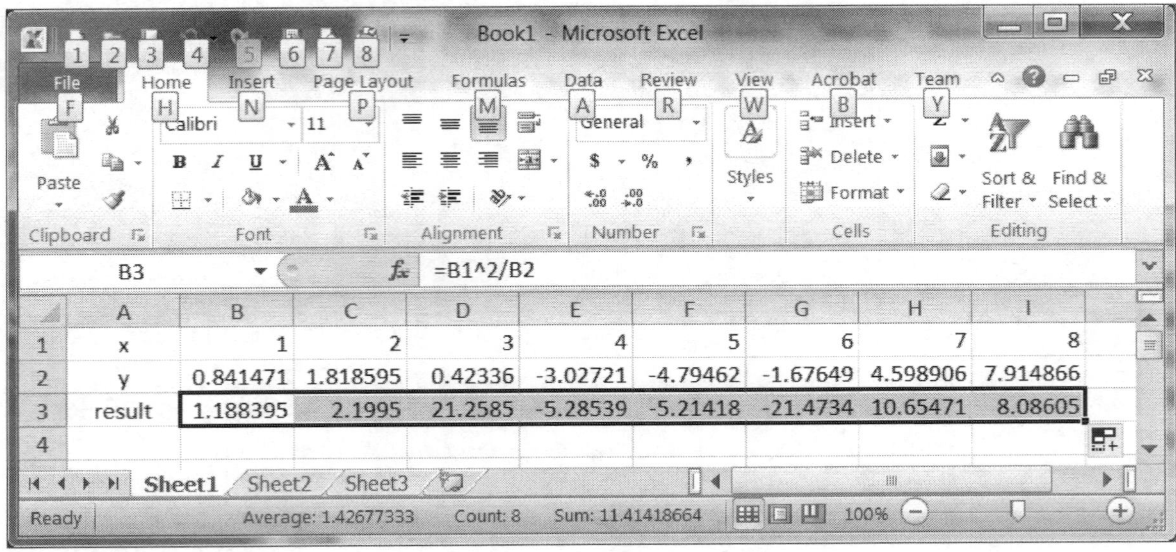


| | A | B | C | D | E | F | G | H | I |
|---|---|---|---|---|---|---|---|---|---|
| 1 | x | 1 | 2 | 3 | 4 | 5 | 6 | 7 | 8 |
| 2 | y | 0.841471 | 1.818595 | 0.42336 | -3.02721 | -4.79462 | -1.67649 | 4.598906 | 7.914866 |
| 3 | result | 1.188395 | 2.1995 | 21.2585 | -5.28539 | -5.21418 | -21.4734 | 10.65471 | 8.08605 |
| 4 | | | | | | | | | |

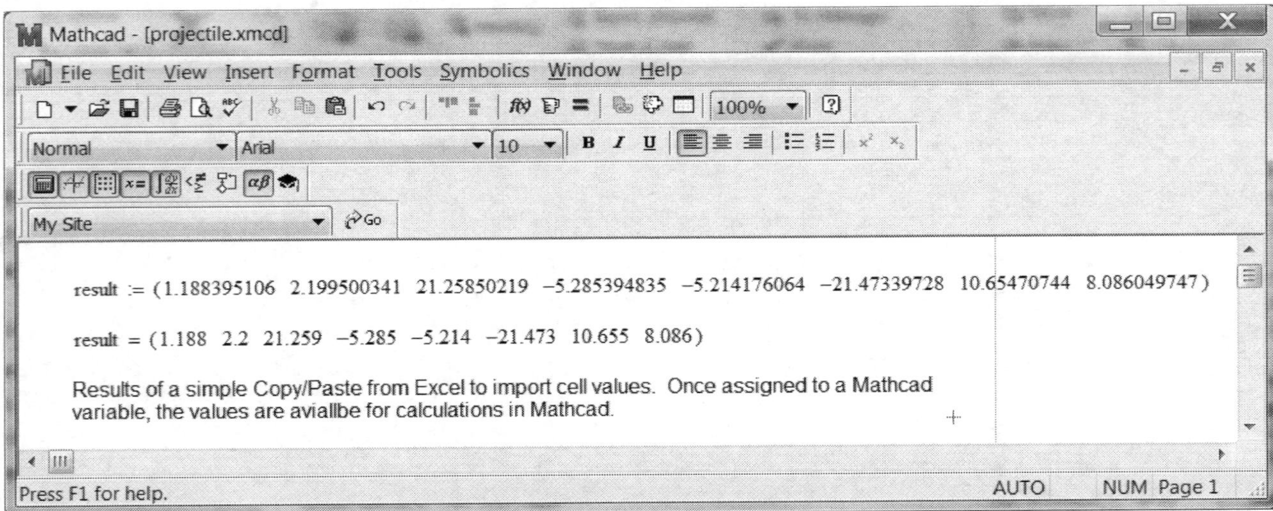

# CHAPTER 4

# Problems and Exercises

The best way to learn the details of a computer application is to use it, and use it a lot. These exercises are designed to reinforce the knowledge gained in the class room or by self-study. In most cases, each problem set can be solved by using any of the tools described in this book. One of the learning objectives is for students to decide which tool is the best for the particular problem, even though any tool might be used. If some of the exercises seem repetitive, this is intentional. Students learn by doing, and practicing these techniques builds a confidence and understanding.

Where possible, students should practice solving the same problem in MATLAB, Mathcad, and the TI-89. This will keep the students versed in the operation of each tool, reinforce the solution method, and illustrate the advantages of a particular tool. Some exercise sets are focused on a specific tool, such as programming in MATLAB. However, most programming problems can also be solved with the TI-89, and even in Mathcad, though lines of code are not involved. The solution algorithm will be the same, only the syntax of the commands is different.

A note about array indexing: Unless otherwise specified, all arrays (vectors, matrices) will begin addressing at (1). Mathcad problems will specify the ORIGIN value.

# EXERCISE 4.1

Defining variables and performing mathematical calculations.

4.1-1. Calculate $22^2 - 1.3^2 + \dfrac{9.8}{\pi^2}$.

4.1-2. Calculate $\log 3.8 + \sqrt{\dfrac{2.9}{1.3^{-0.4}}}$.

4.1-3. Calculate $\dfrac{23.7^{-\frac{1}{3}}(16.7 - e^{0.23})}{6 - 13.6}$.

4.1-4. Calculate $7.9e^{4.3}\left(\sin\dfrac{\pi}{3}\right)$.

4.1-5. Calculate $\sqrt[3]{\cos(40°)\sin(40°)} - \dfrac{\ln(2.5)}{\tan(53°)}$.

Define the variables $x = 6.8$, $y = -2.3$, and $z = 4.1$.

4.1-6. Calculate $x^2 + y^2 + z^2$ and assign the result to a variable $a$.

4.1-7. Calculate $\mathrm{acos}(x^{0.53} + z^{-3.1})$ and assign the result to a variable $b$.

4.1-8. Calculate $\ln x + 2.5y - \dfrac{z^3}{2.5}$ and assign the result to a variable $c$.

4.1-9. Calculate $\log(x - 3)(e^y)$ and assign the result to a variable $h$.

4.1-10. Calculate $\sin^2(x)\left(z^{2.3}\dfrac{\tan(z)}{\cos(y)}\right)$ ($x$, $y$, and $z$ in radians) and assign the result to a variable $t$.

4.1-11. For the triangle in Figure 4.1-1, find the length of side $b$ and the angles $\alpha$ and $\beta$.

4.1-12. For the triangle in Figure 4.1-2, find the length of side $c$ using the law of cosines.

4.1-13. For the triangle in Figure 4.1-2, find the remaining angles using the law of sines.

4.1-14. Given $t = 0.2$, $V = 250$, $R = 250$, $L = 0.45$, evaluate $I = \dfrac{V}{R}\left(1 - e^{-\left(\frac{R}{L}\right)t}\right)$.

4.1-15. Given $t = 4.3$, evaluate $\ln(|t^2 - t^3|)$.

4.1-16. Evaluate $y = 3\sin(x)\cos(x)$, for $x = 37°$, and $x = \dfrac{\pi}{8}$ radians.

4.1-17. Evaluate $\displaystyle\int_2^3 \frac{\ln(u)}{\cos(u)}du$.

4.1-18. Symbolically evaluate $\int x^2\cos(4x)dx$.

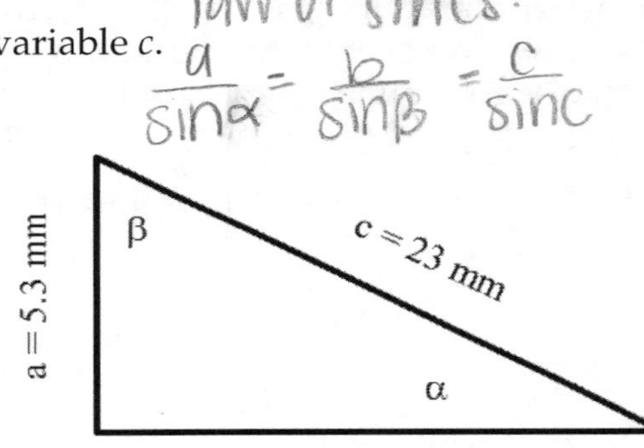


Figure 4.1-1

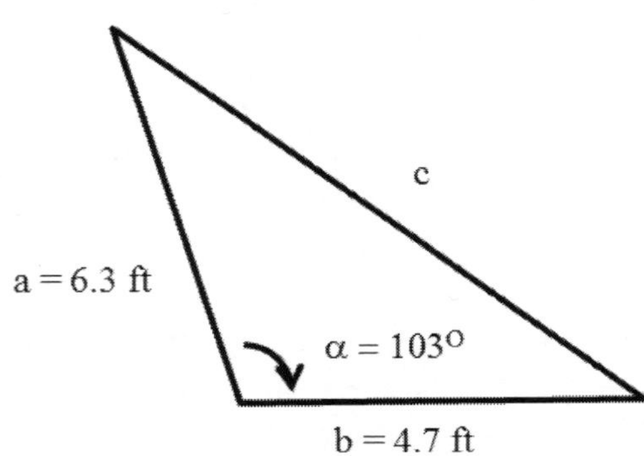


Figure 4.1-2

4.1-19. The equation for combinations of $n$ objects taking $r$ objects at a time is $C_{n,r} = \frac{n!}{r!(n-r)!}$. Find the number of combinations of 13 things taken in groups of 4. Hint: Use the factorial function.

4.1-20. How many different bridge hands (13 cards per hand) can be dealt from a standard deck of 52 cards?

4.1-21. Find the volume of a sphere that has a radius of 4.3 m.

4.1-22. What is the length of the side of a cube that has the same volume as the sphere in Problem 4.1-20?

4.1-23. Find the equation of the line $y = mx + b$, which goes through points (2,4) and (–7,13) in a two-dimensional (2D) coordinate system.

4.1-24. Find the three-dimensional (3D) equation of a line that goes through points (–1,–3,7) and (5,–24,–6).

4.1-25. One form of annuity equation can be used to calculate monthly payment $P$, for a loan balance $B$, number of months $N$, and interest rate per month $i$.

$P = \frac{B*i}{1-(1+i)^{-N}}$. For a balance of \$25,000, and an annual interest rate of 7.5%, determine the monthly payment for a 48-month loan.

4.1-26. Using the annuity equation in Problem 4.1-25, find the loan balance available for a monthly payment of \$500.00, for the same period and interest rate.

4.1-27. A ball is thrown directly vertical with an initial velocity of 10 ft/s. What is the maximum altitude the ball reaches?

4.1-28. The instant just before the ball in Problem 4.1-26 hits the ground, what is its kinetic energy, assuming no air drag?

4.1-29. Symbolically evaluate the integral $\int x^3 e^{-4x} dx$.

4.1-30. Symbolically evaluate the integral $\int x^2 \cos(4x) dx$.

4.1-31. Evaluate the expression $\sin(x) = \sum_{n=0}^{\infty} \frac{(-1)^n x^{(2n+1)}}{(2n+1)!}$, for $x = [2\ 4\ 6]$ radians for the first five values of $n$. Compare results to the $\sin(x)$ function.

# EXERCISE 4.2

This exercise is primarily directed toward the use of the MATLAB colon operator and other vector and *vectorized* (or *element-by-element*) functions.

4.2-1. Create the following vectors:

a. **x** = [1 2 3 4 5]

b. **y** = [4;5;6;7;8]

c. **z** = [1,2,3,4,5]

d. **a** = [1:5]

e. **b** = [1:0.5:5]

f. **c** = [1:10]

g. **c2** = a vector of 11 elements equally spaced from 1 to 10.

4.2-2. Create the following 2D arrays:

a. $x2$ = [2,3;4,5]

b. $y2$ = [−4 7;9 3]

c. $x2 + y2$

d. $d$ = zeros(3,3)

e. $g$ = ones(3,3)

f. $i$ = eye(3).

4.2-3. Determine elements in an array:

a. What is the third element of $x$?

b. What is the element in row 1, column 2 of $x2$?

c. What is the element in row 1, column 1 of $y2$?

4.2-4. Address elements in an array:

a. What are all the elements in column 2 of $x2$?

b. What are all the elements in row 1 of $y2$?

4.2-5. Adding elements to an array:

a. Change the third element of $x$ to 12.

b. Make the eighth element of $x = 88$.

c. Make the fifth row, fifth column element of $x2 = 5$.

d. Make $y2$ the fourth and fifth row/column of $x2$.

e. What are elements 4–6 of $x$?

f. Show all the rows of columns 1 and 2 of $x2$.

g. Show all the columns of rows 3 and 4 of $x2$.

h. Show the first and second columns of rows 3 and 4 of $x2$.

4.2-6. Deleting elements from an array:

a. Delete element 3 from $x$.

b. Delete element 3,4 from $y$.

c. Delete all the columns of rows 3 and 4 from $x2$.

4.2-7. Create the row vector **x** = [6 5 4 3 2].

4.2-8. Create a vector **y** that starts at 0 and goes to 100 in increments of 0.2.

4.2-9. Create a column vector **z** that has four elements of any value.

4.2-10. Create a vector **w** that starts with 3, ends with 24, and has 33 elements.

4.2-11. What is the value of the 20th element of **y**?

4.2-12. Create a vector **d** made up of the 13th thru 19th element of **w**.

4.2-13. Create a $6 \times 6$ array $g$ of all elements = 6.

4.2-14. Create a $2 \times 2$ array $x2$ of any value.

4.2-15. Increase the size of $x2$ such that element row 5, column 6 = 8.

4.2-16. Create a $2 \times 3$ array $y2$ such that row 1 is all 1s and row 2 is all 0s. Do not type individual elements explicitly.

4.2-17. Create matrix $A$ by typing one command. Do not type individual elements explicitly.

$$A = \begin{bmatrix} 0 & 0 & 0 \\ 0 & 0 & 0 \\ 0 & 0 & 0 \\ 0 & 3 & 3 \\ 0 & 3 & 3 \end{bmatrix}$$

4.2-18. Create matrix $B$ by typing one command. Do not type individual elements explicitly.

$$B = \begin{bmatrix} 0 & 0 & 0 \\ 0 & 0 & 0 \\ 0 & 1 & 6 \\ 0 & 2 & 4 \\ 0 & 3 & 2 \end{bmatrix}$$

4.2-19. Create matrix $C$ by extracting it from matrix $B$.

$$C = \begin{bmatrix} 1 & 6 \\ 2 & 4 \end{bmatrix}$$

4.2-20. Create $D = B^T$ from 2 to 18.

4.2-21. Create a row vector **a** that contains the elements of row 2 of matrix $D$ from Problem 4.2-20.

4.2-22. Create a row vector **b** that contains the second thru fifth element of row 3 of matrix $D$.

4.2-23. In matrix $A$, change the value of the element $a_{42}$ to be −5.

4.2-24. Create matrix $E = \begin{bmatrix} 1 & 6 & 1 & 0 \\ 2 & 4 & 0 & 1 \end{bmatrix}$ from matrix C and the eye() command.

4.2-25. Change matrix $B$ to be $B = \begin{bmatrix} 1 & 6 \\ 2 & 4 \\ 3 & 2 \end{bmatrix}$.

4.2-26. Create the following arrays in MATLAB:

$$x = \begin{bmatrix} -2 & 3 & 6 \end{bmatrix} \; y = \begin{bmatrix} 12 & 13 & 5 \end{bmatrix} \; A = \begin{bmatrix} 1 & 0 & 1 \\ 2 & 3 & 2 \\ -7 & -1 & 1 \end{bmatrix} \; B = \begin{bmatrix} 4 & -3 & 1 \\ -3 & 1 & 6 \\ 1 & -2 & 7 \end{bmatrix}$$

a. Add 3 to each element of $x$ and $y$.
b. Multiply each element of $A$ by –2.
c. Multiply each element of $x$ and $y$ together to create a vector **z**.
d. Square each element of $y$.
e. Create a $3 \times 3$ matrix $C$ such that each element is 3 raised to power by the respective elements in $B$.
f. Find the average of all the elements in $x$.
g. Evaluate the following expression: $t = \sin^2(x) * \cos(y) / \left(2 * \sqrt{x + 2.5}\right)$.
h. Find the maximum and minimum elements in each column of $A$.
i. Find the maximum and minimum elements in each row of $B$ and store the results in variables $v$ and $w$.
j. Find the magnitude of the vector **y**.
k. Find the absolute value of the vector **x**.
l. Add the three rows of matrix $A$ together and store the result in vector **d**.
m. Multiply the elements of $x$ by the maximum value of **d**.
n. Calculate the sum of the first column of $A$.
o. Multiply the third row of $A$ by the second column of $B$ (element by element).

4.2-27. Create a matrix $C = \begin{bmatrix} 3 & 3 & 3 & 1 & 0 & 0 \\ 3 & 3 & 3 & 0 & 1 & 0 \\ 3 & 3 & 3 & 0 & 0 & 1 \end{bmatrix}$.

a. Verify the order of matrix C by using the size() function.
b. Notice that size() returns two values as a vector. Execute the size() function again and assign its result to the vector [row col]. Note how the variables appear in the workspace window.
c. Create a vector **a** from row 2 of matrix C and verify the number of elements using the length() function.
d. Create a matrix $B$ of six rows and three columns from the elements of matrix C using the reshape() function.
e. Create a matrix $D$ of two rows and nine columns from the elements of matrix C using the reshape() function.
f. Create a square matrix where vector **a** is the element of the diagonal.
g. Create a vector from the diagonal elements of $B$.

4.2-28. Strings. A variable containing the value of characters (text) is also a vector (or array).

a. Create a variable s1 that contains the string "My name is ". Note the space before the closing double quote.
b. Using your first and last name, create a variable s2 that is a string variable of your name.
c. Create a variable s3 that combines s1 and s2 into a single sentence.
d. Use an array function to determine the number of characters in variable s3.
e. Create a new string variable n1 from variable s2 that is just your first name.
f. Delete your last name and the preceding space character from variable s3.

g. Enter the following command: s4 = char('My name is', s2)

h. What is the size of s4? What is the length of row 1? Why?

4.2-29. For $A = \begin{bmatrix} 2 & -3 \\ 1 & 0 \\ -6 & 7 \end{bmatrix}$ and $C = \begin{bmatrix} 4 & 6 \\ 8 & -2 \\ 2 & 4 \end{bmatrix}$, what MATLAB command produces $D = \begin{bmatrix} 8 & -2 \\ 2 & -3 \\ 1 & 0 \\ -6 & 7 \end{bmatrix}$ from matrices $A$ and $C$?

4.2-30. Given $A = \begin{bmatrix} 1 & 3 & 5 & 7 & 9 & 11 \\ 0 & 5 & 10 & 15 & 20 & 25 \\ 10 & 20 & 30 & 40 & 50 & 60 \\ 67 & 2 & 43 & 68 & 4 & 13 \end{bmatrix}$

a. What MATLAB command will let you know the order of matrix $A$?

b. What is the value $a_{3,4}$?

c. Given $B$ is the transpose of $A$, what is the value $b_{3,4}$?

d. What would you enter on the TI-89 to create $B$ in the previous question?

e. What would you type in MATLAB to create a vector **c** consisting of the elements in the second column of $A$?

f. What command would you type in MATLAB to create a vector **d,** which contains the elements in $A$ in rows 2–3 and columns 3–5.

g. What command would you type in MATLAB to add two columns to matrix $A$ with 9 in row 4, column 8 and 0s in the other elements in the new columns? Do not type individual elements explicitly.

h. Using the colon operator, write the command you would type in MATLAB to create a vector **x** having a regular spacing of 0.2 starting at 2 and ending at 14.

4.2-31. If s1 = 'Today is' and s2 = 'Friday', what is the MATLAB command shortcut to create s1 = Today is Friday?

4.2-32. Write the MATLAB command to create a column vector that starts with –2.8 and ends with 34.6 and has 11 elements.

4.2-33. Show the MATLAB command to create the following matrix by typing one command. Do not type individual elements explicitly.

$$D = \begin{bmatrix} 0 & 0 & 0 & 0 & 0 \\ 0 & 0 & 0 & 6 & 6 \\ 0 & 0 & 0 & 6 & 6 \end{bmatrix}$$

4.2-34. Show the MATLAB command to create $V = [-3 \quad 34 \quad 2]$ from $V = [-3 \quad 14 \quad 34 \quad 2]$.

4.2-35. Show the single MATLAB command to create $M = \begin{bmatrix} 0 & 0 \\ 0 & 0 \\ 1 & 1 \\ 1 & 1 \end{bmatrix}$.

4.2-36. Using the colon operator/symbol, create a row vector called **a3**, which has five elements that are all −3.

4.2-37. For $A = \begin{bmatrix} 2 & -3 \\ 1 & 0 \\ -6 & 7 \end{bmatrix}$ and $x = \begin{bmatrix} 3 & 5 & 7 \end{bmatrix}$, show the MATLAB command to append the vector **x** as column 3 of matrix $A$.

# EXERCISE 4.3 NUMERICAL SOLUTIONS

Finding roots, solving nonexplicit equations, and systems of equations.

4.3-1. Find the roots of $f(x) = 4x^3 + 3x^2 + 8x + 12$.

4.3-2. Solve $20\log\left(t^{2.5} - \sin\left(\frac{t}{3}\right)\right) = t - 9$ for $t$.

4.3-3. Solve the following equation for $f_0$:

$$20\log\left(\frac{\sqrt{(f_0 - 20) + 5}}{\sqrt{f_0} + 5}\right) = -30$$

4.3-4. Use a Mathcad "Given, Find" block to solve the following system of equations:

$$\frac{V_1}{15} + \frac{V_2 - V_1}{10} = -3$$
$$V_3 - V_1 = 10$$
$$\frac{V_1 - 10}{30} + \frac{V_2}{30} + \frac{V_3 - 20}{10} = 2$$

4.3-5. Use Given . . . Find to find the roots of $x^3 - 2x^2 - 8x + 1 = 0$.

4.3-6. Solve $\ln(x+1) = \left(\frac{x}{4}\right)^2$ for $x > 0$.

4.3-7. Find the complex solutions (roots).

a. $x^2 - 4x + 5 = 0$

b. $3x^2 + 2x + 2 = 0$

c. $z^4 - 2iz^2 + 4 = 0$

4.3-8. For the circle segment in Figure 4.3-1, find the angle $\theta$ (degrees) shown so that the area $A = 15$ m² when radius $r = 30$ m. Then find the total length of the perimeter.

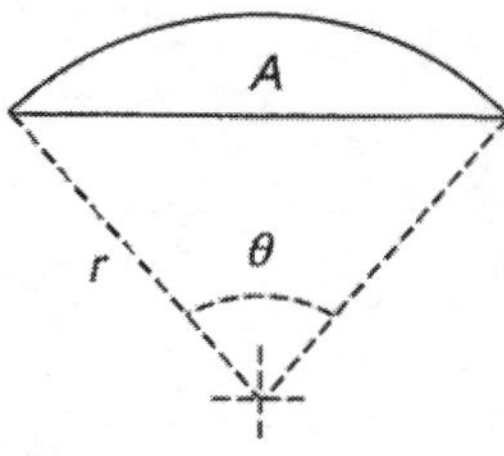


Figure 4.3-1

# EXERCISE 4.4 MATRIX OPERATION AND MATRIX ALGEBRA

4.4-1. For each matrix, identify the order and the value of the element specified. (The intent is to use the functions available in the computer tool.)

For $A = \begin{bmatrix} 2 & 3 & 4 \\ 0 & -2 & 7 \\ 1 & 2 & -2 \end{bmatrix}$, find $a_{32}$, $a_{13}$.

For $B = \begin{bmatrix} -1 & 6 & 0 \\ 2 & 4 & 6 \end{bmatrix}$, find $b_{21}$, $b_{13}$.

For $C = \begin{bmatrix} 7 & 5 & 3 & 0 & -3 \\ 2 & 3 & 5 & 7 & 0 \\ 0 & 8 & -3 & 6 & -7 \\ 5 & 2 & 1 & 0 & 8 \end{bmatrix}$, find $c_{44}$, $c_{23}$.

4.4-2. Given the following matrices,

$$L = \begin{bmatrix} 6 & 2 & 9 \\ 1 & 8 & 3 \\ 7 & 4 & 5 \end{bmatrix} \qquad M = \begin{bmatrix} 2 & 1 & 4 & 4 & 1 \\ -7 & 3 & 2 & -3 & 3 \end{bmatrix} \qquad N = \begin{bmatrix} 5 & -3 \\ 4 & 2 \\ 1 & 8 \end{bmatrix}$$

determine whether the indicated operation is legal, and if so, what is the order of the result?

a. $L \times N$

b. $M \times L$

c. $N \times L$

d. $L \times N \times M$

4.4-3. If $A = B$, find $x$ and $y$:

$$A = \begin{bmatrix} -1 & 6 & 0 \\ 2 & 4 & 6 \end{bmatrix} \qquad B = \begin{bmatrix} x-y & 6 & 0 \\ 2 & y^2 & 6 \end{bmatrix}$$

4.4-4. Given $A$, $B$, and $C$, show that $A(B+C) = AB + AC$.

$$A = \begin{bmatrix} 1 & 2 & 1 \\ -3 & 1 & -2 \\ 0 & 2 & 1 \\ 4 & 1 & 3 \end{bmatrix} \qquad B = \begin{bmatrix} -3 & -1 & 0 & 4 \\ 3 & 0 & 2 & 7 \\ 1 & 4 & -6 & 1 \end{bmatrix} \qquad C = \begin{bmatrix} 0 & 2 & 3 & 4 \\ -4 & 1 & 3 & 5 \\ 1 & 3 & 5 & 7 \end{bmatrix}$$

4.4-5. Given $A$, $B$, and $C$, show that $(BA)C = B(AC)$.

$$A = \begin{bmatrix} 1 & 2 & 1 \\ -3 & 1 & -2 \\ 0 & 2 & 1 \\ 4 & 1 & 3 \end{bmatrix} \qquad B = \begin{bmatrix} -3 & -1 & 0 & 4 \\ 3 & 0 & 2 & 7 \\ 1 & 4 & -6 & 1 \end{bmatrix} \qquad C = \begin{bmatrix} 1 & 0 & 2 \\ 2 & 4 & -5 \\ -5 & 1 & 3 \end{bmatrix}$$

4.4-6. Given matrix $A$, show $AA^{T}$ and $A^{T}A$.

$$A = \begin{bmatrix} 1 & -1 & 0 & 1 & 1 \\ 0 & 2 & -1 & -1 & 0 \\ 2 & 1 & 0 & -1 & -2 \\ -1 & 0 & 1 & 2 & 3 \\ -2 & -3 & -2 & -1 & 2 \end{bmatrix}$$

4.4-7. Given the matrix $A$ in Problem 4.4-6, find a matrix $B$, such that $A + B = I_3$.

4.4-8. Evaluate the determinants of the following matrices:

$$\begin{bmatrix} 3 & -1 \\ -2 & 2 \end{bmatrix} \qquad \begin{bmatrix} 1 & -1 & 3 \\ 2 & 0 & 3 \\ -2 & 1 & 1 \end{bmatrix} \qquad \begin{bmatrix} -2 & 1 & 0 & 3 \\ 0 & -1 & 0 & 7 \\ 1 & 2 & 0 & -2 \\ 3 & -1 & 2 & 2 \end{bmatrix}$$

4.4-9. Without evaluating, examine the following matrices and explain why the determinants are 0:

$$\begin{bmatrix} 1 & -1 & 1 \\ 2 & 0 & 2 \\ -2 & 1 & -2 \end{bmatrix} \qquad \begin{bmatrix} 1 & -1 & 3 \\ 2 & 0 & 3 \\ 1 & 1 & 0 \end{bmatrix} \qquad \begin{bmatrix} 1 & -1 & 3 \\ -6 & 3 & 12 \\ -2 & 1 & 14 \end{bmatrix}$$

4.4-10. Create the following arrays and assign them to the variable names:

$$A = \begin{bmatrix} -2 & 3 & 6 \end{bmatrix} \qquad B = \begin{bmatrix} 12 & 13 & 5 \end{bmatrix} \qquad C = \begin{bmatrix} 3 & 0 & -1 \\ 2 & 7 & 5 \end{bmatrix}$$

$$D = \begin{bmatrix} 2 & -5 \\ 0 & 1 \\ 9 & 3 \end{bmatrix} \qquad E = \begin{bmatrix} 1 & 0 & 1 \\ 2 & 3 & 2 \\ -7 & -1 & 1 \end{bmatrix} \qquad F = \begin{bmatrix} 4 & -3 & 1 \\ -3 & 1 & 6 \\ 1 & -2 & 7 \end{bmatrix}$$

a. Calculate $B*D$ and assign the value to the variable bd.
b. Calculate $C*D$ and assign the value to the variable cd.
c. Calculate $D*C$ and assign the value to the variable dc.
d. Calculate $A*B^{T}$.
e. Calculate $A^{T}*B$.
f. Find the determinant of matrices $E$ and $F$.
g. Find the sum of $C^{T} + D$.
h. Find the inverses of matrices $E$ and $F$.
i. Change row 1 of matrix $F$ to be [–5 2 4] using a single command in MATLAB.
j. Change row 1 of matrix $F$ to be [–5 2 4] using the matrix editor in the TI-89.

# EXERCISE 4.5 COMPLEX NUMBERS

4.5-1. Express the following in standard form:

a. $(2+3i)+(-1+2i)$

b. $(2+3i)(-1+2i)$

c. $\frac{1}{(3-i)}$

d. $\frac{(2+3i)(-1+2i)}{(3-i)}$

4.5-2. Given $z_1 = 3-2i$ and $z_2 = 2+i$, express the following in standard form:

a. $z_1 + z_2$

b. $z_1 * z_2$

c. $z_1 / z_2^2$

4.5-3. Given $z_1 = 3-i$ and $z_2 = 1+2i$, find the complex conjugates:

a. $\overline{z_1 + z_2}$

b. $\overline{z_1 * z_2}$

c. $\overline{z_1 / z_2}$

4.5-4. Given $z = -1+2i$, find the following complex numbers and plot them on an Argand diagram:

a. $\bar{z}$

b. $z^2$

c. $\frac{z}{\bar{z}}$

d. $\frac{1}{z}$

4.5-5. Given $z_1 = 6.4+3i$ and $z_2 = 4.3e^{2.5i}$, express the results of the following equations in exponential form:

a. $z_1 + \bar{z}_2$

b. $z_1(z_2)^3$

c. $\frac{z_2}{z_1 - \bar{z}_1}$

d. $|z_1| z_2$

e. $\overline{z_1 + z_2}$

4.5-6. Find modulus and principal argument of the following complex numbers:

a. $z_1 = -1+i$

b. $z_3 = -4$

c. $z_2 = 3-2i$

d. $z_4 = -4i$

4.5-7. Given $z_1 = 3 - 2i$ and $z_2 = 2 + i$, express each in polar form.

4.5-8. Find all of the roots of $z^5 = 4 - 4i$. Express the results in both standard and polar forms.

4.5-9. Find the modulus and principal argument of $z = 9.3e^{(-2+4i)}$.

4.5-10. For $z_2 = 2.5e^{(2+1.2i)}(2 - 3i)e^{0.5i}$, find the following:

a. $z$ in standard form
b. $z$ in polar form
c. $z$ in exponential form
d. Re($z$)
e. Im($z$)
f. mod($z$)
g. arg($z$)
h. conj($z$)

4.5-11. Given arg($z$) = 3 radians and mod($z$) = 5 radians, find the following:

a. $z$ in standard form
b. $z$ in polar form
c. $z$ in exponential form
d. Re($z$)
e. Im($z$)
f. conj($z$)

# EXERCISE 4.6 SOLVING SYSTEMS OF LINEAR EQUATIONS

4.6-1. For the following system of linear equations, $\begin{matrix} 4x-2y=8 \\ 2x+8y=4 \end{matrix}$, convert to form $A\bar{x}=\bar{d}$, then find the inverse of $A$ and solve for $x,y$.

4.6-2. Solve the following system for the unknowns using the $A\bar{x}=\bar{d}$ form:

$$\begin{aligned} 12x-5y&=11 \\ -3x+4y+7z&=-3 \\ 6x+2y+3z&=22 \end{aligned}$$

4.6-3. Convert the following system to an augmented matrix and solve it using Gaussian elimination (reduced row echelon form):

a. $\begin{aligned} 2x+y+5z&=13 \\ x-y+2z&=-1 \\ x+y+z&=4 \end{aligned}$

b. $\begin{aligned} x-2y+5z&=2 \\ 2x+y-7z&=6 \\ x-y-z&=1 \end{aligned}$

4.6-4. Given the augmented matrix, what type of solution is represented?

$$\begin{bmatrix} 28 & -7 & 14 & 2 \\ 1 & 2 & -4 & 2 \\ 4 & 1 & -2 & 2 \end{bmatrix}$$

4.6-5. Determine the solution to the following system. What type of solution results? What is the Cartesian equation of the line represented by this solution? What is the rank of [$A$]? What is the rank of [$A$ $d$]? How does rank[$A$] = rank[$A$ $d$] indicate the solution? What is the pseudo-inverse solution?

a. $\begin{aligned} x-2y+3z&=2 \\ 2x-y+2z&=3 \\ x+y-z&=1 \end{aligned}$

b. $\begin{aligned} x+y-zz&=1 \\ 3x-y+3z&=5 \\ x-y+2z&=2 \end{aligned}$

4.6-6. Solve the following systems for the unknowns:

a. $\begin{aligned} 1-9x-8y+z&=0 \\ 7x+7y&=20 \\ 6x-7y+2z&=10 \end{aligned}$

b. $\begin{aligned} x+y+z&=1 \\ 2x-y+2z&=3 \\ x-3y-z&=1 \end{aligned}$

$$x + 2y - z = 4$$

c. $2x + 10y + 2z = 10$

$$x + 5y + 3z = 11$$

4.6-7. Find the set of values for $a$ and $b$ that have a (i) unique solution, (ii) infinite solutions, and (iii) no solution:

$$3x + 4y + z = 4$$
$$2x - y + z = 3$$
$$x - 3y + az = b$$

4.6-8. Find the nontrivial solution for the following set of equations:

$$-3x + 2y - z = 0$$
$$2x - 3y - z = 0$$
$$-x - y - 2z = 0$$

4.6-9. The currents ($i$) in the electrical circuit shown are unknown. The circuit is analyzed by summing voltages around each loop and knowing that $\sum$ voltage in a loop = 0 and voltage = current × resistance, the following equations result:

Left loop: $-V_1 + R_2(i_1 - i_2) + R_4(i_1 - i_3) = 0$
Upper loop: $R_1 i_2 + R_3(i_2 - i_3) + R_2(i_2 - i_1) = 0$
Right loop: $R_3(i_3 - i_2) + R_5 i_3 + R_4(i_3 - i_1) = 0$

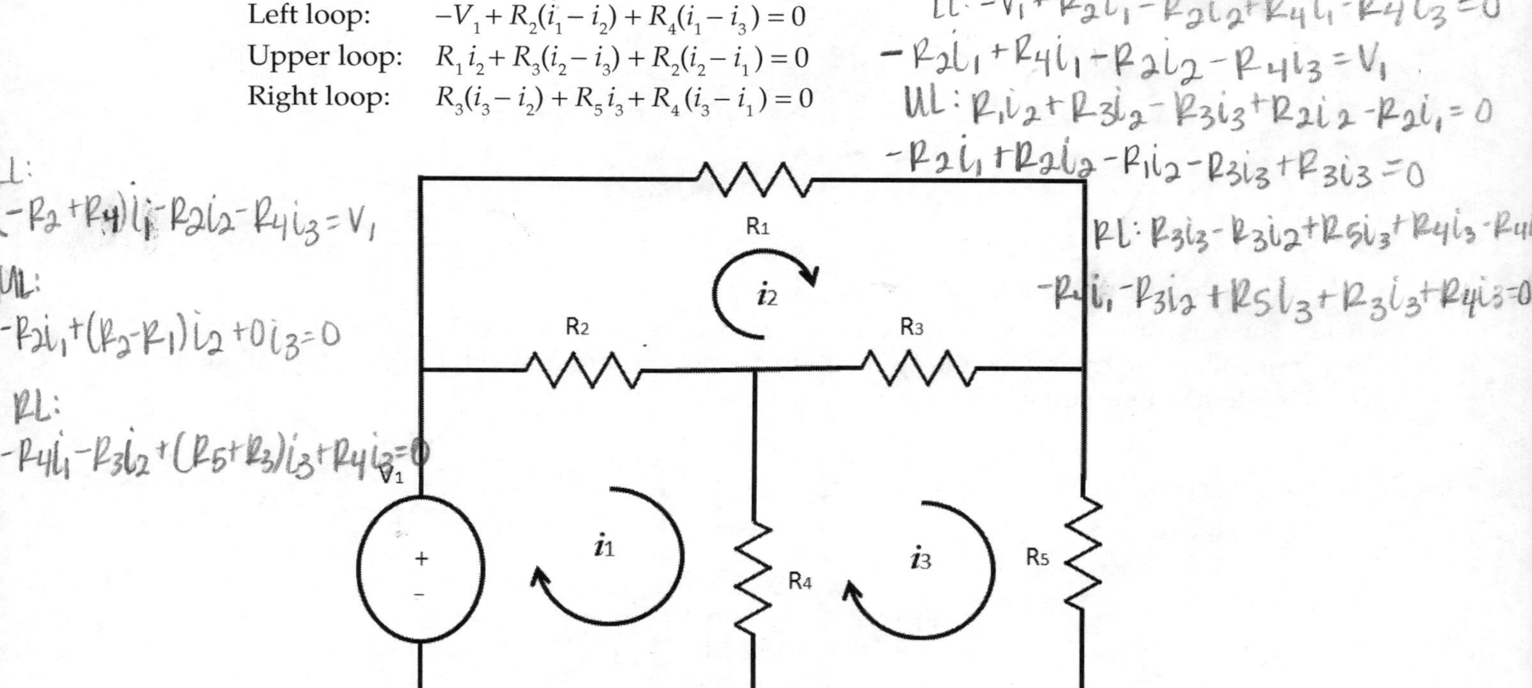


Arrange the equations in $A\bar{x} = \bar{d}$ form, and solve for the currents using the following values:

$$R_1 = 2, R_2 = 4, R_3 = 6, R_4 = 8, R_5 = 10, V = 10$$

4.6-10. Given the following electric circuit equations:

$$4i_1 - i_2 - i_3 = 12$$
$$-i_1 + R \cdot i_2 = 24$$
$$i_1 + 5i_2 = -12$$

For $i_2 = 2\,\text{A}$, find the value of $R$ that satisfies the equations.

4.6-11. A $5 \times 8$-ft sign weighs 270 lb and is supported by two cables and a ball-and-socket joint at $A$. Using the theory of static equilibrium, the tension forces in the cables $T_{BD}$ and $T_{CE}$ and the three reaction forces at $A$, $A_X$, $A_Y$, and $A_Z$, can be determined by the following linear equations:

$$A_X - \tfrac{2}{3}T_{BD} - \tfrac{6}{7}T_{CE} = 0$$
$$A_Y + \tfrac{1}{3}T_{BD} + \tfrac{3}{7}T_{CE} - 270 = 0$$
$$A_Z - \tfrac{2}{3}T_{BD} + \tfrac{2}{7}T_{CE} = 0$$
$$2.667T_{BD} + 2.571T_{CE} - 1080 = 0$$
$$5.333T_{BD} - 1.714T_{CE} = 0$$

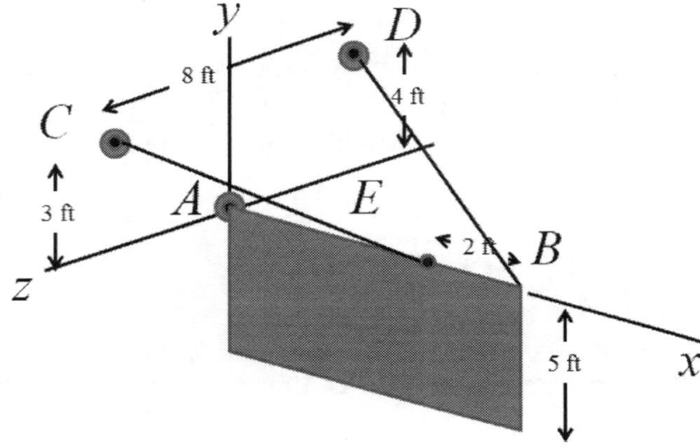


Solve for the unknown variables $A_X$, $A_Y$, $A_Z$, $T_{BD}$, and $T_{CE}$.

4.6-12. The truss structure shown is made of members joined at the ends. The forces in the nine members are created by the applied forces and are determined by solving the following system of nine equations:

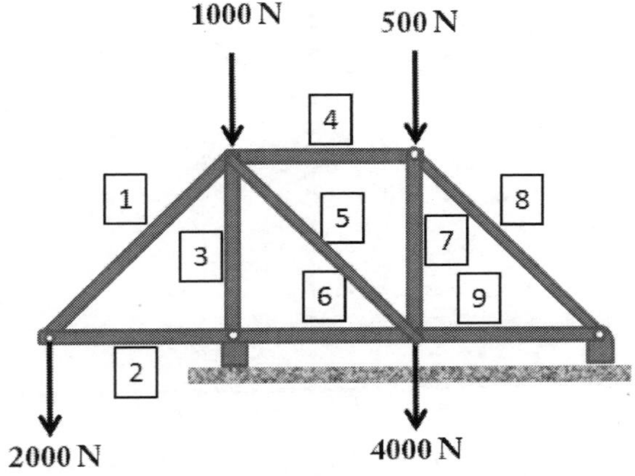

$$\cos(45°)F_1 + F_2 = 0$$
$$F_4 + \cos(48.81°)F_5 - \cos(45°)F_1 = 0$$
$$-\sin(48.81°)F_5 - F_3 - \sin(45°)\,F_1 = 1000$$
$$\cos(48.81°)F_8 - F_4 = 0$$
$$-\sin(48.81°)F_8 - F_7 = 500$$
$$F_9 - \cos(48.81°)F_5 - F_6 = 0$$
$$F_7 + \sin(48.81°)F_5 = 4000$$
$$\sin(48.81°)F_8 = -1107.14$$
$$-\cos(48.81°)F_8 + F_9 = 0$$

Write the equations in matrix form and solve for the forces in the members. A positive force means the member is in tension and a negative force means in compression.

# EXERCISE 4.7 RELATIONAL AND LOGICAL OPERATORS AND THEIR MATHEMATICAL OPERATIONS

4.7-1. For $x = [6,3,9]$ and $y = [14,2,9]$,

a. Find all values of $x$ less than $y$.
b. Find all values of $x$ greater than $y$.
c. Find all values of $x$ not equal to $y$.
d. Find all values of $x$ equal to $y$.
e. Find all values of $x$ greater than 8.

4.7-2. Evaluate

a. $z = 6 > 3 + 8$
b. $z = 6 + 3 > 8$
c. $z = 4 > (2 + 9)$
d. $z = (4 < 7) + 3$
e. $z = 4 < 7 + 3$
f. $z = (4 < 7) \times 5$
g. $z = 4 < (7 \times 5)$
h. $z = 2/5 \geq 5$

4.7-3. For $x = [-9,-6,0,2,5]$ and $y = [-10,-6,2,4,6]$,

a. Find all values of $x$ less than $y$.
b. Find all values of $x$ greater than $y$.
c. Find all values of $x$ not equal to $y$.
d. Find all values of $x$ equal to $y$.
e. Find all values of $x$ greater than 2.

4.7-4. For $x = [-2,0,4]$, what is the result of $y = \text{find}(x)$?

4.7-5. For $x = [-4,-1,0,2,10]$ and $y = [-5,-2,2,5,9]$, find the values and indices of the elements in $x$ that are greater than the corresponding elements in $y$.

4.7-6. For $x = [5,13,18,4]$ and $y = [-9,13,7,4]$, determine

a. $z \cong y > x$
b. $z = x \,\&\, y$
c. $z = x \mid y$
d. $z = x \text{ or } (x,y)$

4.7-7. For $x = [-3,0,0,2,5,8]$ and $y = [-5,-2,0,3,4,10]$, determine

a. $z = y \lesssim x$
b. $z = x \,\&\, y$
c. $z = x \mid y$
d. $z = x \text{ or } (x,y)$

4.7-8. For $x = [-9,-6,0,2,5]$ and $y = [-10,-6,2,4,6]$, determine

a. $z = (x < y)$

b. $z = (x > y)$

c. $z = (x \cong y)$

d. $z = (x \equiv y)$

e. $z = (x > 2)$

4.7-9. For $x = [-3,0,0,2,5,8,-5,-2,0,3,4,10]$, what is $z$ for $z = \text{find}(x < 0 \mid x \geq 8)$?

4.7-10. For $x = [-3\ 0\ 0\ 2\ 5\ 8]$ and $y = [-5\ -2\ 0\ 3\ 4\ 10]$,

a. What is $\sim x$?

b. What is $y \lesssim x$?

c. What is find($x$ & $y$)?

## EXERCISE 4.8 BASIC PROGRAMMING EXERCISES

These problems are primarily intended to be solved in MATLAB, but can be programmed in the TI-89, or any computer programming language.

4.8-1. Write a program that defines two variables, performs basic mathematical operations, such as multiplication, division, and exponentiation, and displays the results.

4.8-2. Write a program that defines two variables, performs trigonometric and logarithmic operations, and displays the results.

4.8-3. Write a program that defines a vector variable with six elements and a vector variable with four elements. For each vector, find the sum of all elements, the average of all elements, the smallest element, and the largest element.

4.8-4. Write a program that inputs any number and divides it by 7. If the quotient is a fraction, the display should be "The answer is a fraction", otherwise, it should be "The answer is not a fraction".

4.8-5. Write a program using a for loop that displays all the even numbers up to and including 20.

4.8-6. Write a program using a for loop that displays the series of numbers 3,7,11,15,19.

4.8-7. Write a program using a for loop that displays the series of numbers −1,−3,−5,−7,−9,−11,−13.

4.8-8. Write a program that defines $x = 4$, then use a for loop to find the sum of $x + x^2 + x^3 + x^4$.

4.8-9. Write a program using a while loop that inputs a positive integer, stops when 0 is entered, and finds the average of the integers.

4.8-10. Write a program that inputs any positive integer, and using a while loop, continuously takes the square root of the successive results until the difference between successive results is less than 1. Show the number of times the loop was executed.

4.8-11. Write a program using a case structure to display a letter grade if a numerical grade is entered. Use the range 90–100 = *A*, 80–89 = *B*, 70–79 = *C*, 60–69 = *D*, and <60 = *F*.

4.8-12. Write a program that inputs a vector of any length and then uses a for loop to display the elements of the vector in reverse order.

4.8-13. Write a program using a while loop that generates a random number between 0 and 1 each time in the loop and terminates the loop when the random number is less than 0.30. Display the number of times the loop executed.

4.8-14. For the following program segment:

```
x=.23;
for k=2:3:13
   x=x+x*k;
end
%......
```

a. How many times is the for loop executed?

b. What is the value of *x* after this segment executes?

# EXERCISE 4.9 CREATING PLOTS AND GRAPHS

4.9-1. Define and graph the function $g(x) = x\sin(3\pi x)$.

4.9-2. Define $y = \sin(x)$ and plot in the range $0 - 4\pi$.

4.9-3. Define $y = \sin(2x)$ and $z = e^{(-0.5x)}$ and plot on the same graph in the range $0 - 2\pi$.

4.9-4. Define $y = \sin(nx)$ and plot three subplots on the same graph for $n = 2,4,6$ in the range $0 - 2\pi$.

4.9-5. Plot both $x(t)$ and $f(t)$ on the same graph. Label the $y$-axis as "displacements", label the $x$-axis as "time", and title the graph as "trajectory".

$$x(t) = \frac{1}{2}at^2, \quad f(t) = -(2.5t)^2 + 35t, \quad a := -9.8, \quad 0 \le t \le 10$$

4.9-6. Generate an $x$–$y$ plot of $g(x) = \cos(2\pi x)$. Change the $x$-axis scale to go from $x = -2$ to $x = 2$.

4.9-7. Given the list of grades, create a Mathcad histogram that shows the number of *A*s (90–100), *B*s (80–90), *C*s (70–80), and *D*s (60–70).

77,68,72,66,88,86,89,81,60,90,89,63,72,69,70,63,83,72,92,94,86,96,98,80,83,72,67,84

4.9-8. A particle moves along a straight line, and the position as a function of time is given as follows:

$$x(t) = 0.41t^4 - 10.8t^3 + 64t^2 - 8.2t + 4\,\text{ft}$$

Derive the expressions for velocity and acceleration of the particle and plot the position, velocity, and acceleration as functions of time for $0 \le t \le 8$ s.

Plot all three curves on the graph with different line styles and/or markers. Label the axes appropriately and include units. Put a title and a legend on the plot.

4.9-9. The height $h(t)$ and horizontal distance $x(t)$ traveled by a ball thrown at an angle $A$ with velocity $v$ are governed by the following equations:

$$h(t) = vt \cdot \sin(A) - \frac{1}{2}gt^2, \; x(t) = vt \cdot \cos(A)$$

Given $g = 9.81$ m/s$^2$ and $v = 10$ m/s, plot the trajectories (i.e., $h$ vs. $x$) for three values of the angle $A$ (20°, 45°, and 70°) on the same figure. Use different line styles (not markers) to indicate which plot represents which value of $A$. Label the $x$-axis and the $y$-axis with appropriate axis titles (including units). Make sure that you only plot each trajectory from the moment it is thrown (assume $h(0) = 0$ m, at $t = 0$) to the moment it hits the ground ($h(t) = 0$ m again!). Note: You will be plotting $x(t)$ on the $x$-axis and $h(t)$ on the $y$-axis. Hint: You will also need to know the total time of flight $t_{hit}$, *for each angle.*

4.9-10. Write a MATLAB program (script file) that produces Figure 4.9-1. Using a range of $0 \le t \le 10$, $y = 2.5e^{(-0.2t)}\cos(2\pi * n * t)$, where $n = 2, 4, 6$. You must use a loop structure rather than repeating commands. Create the figure exactly as shown using either commands or the figure editor.

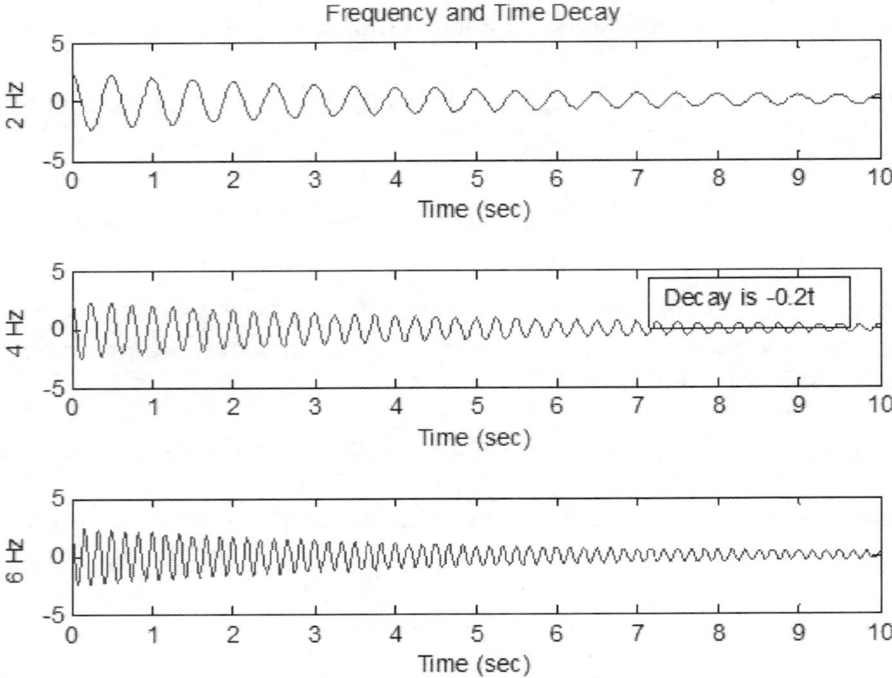


**Figure 4.9-1**

# EXERCISE 4.10 PROGRAMMING EXERCISES TO SOLVE ENGINEERING TYPE PROBLEMS

4.10-1. Write a program that flips a coin 100 times and then displays the number of heads and the number of tails. As the probability of a heads or tails is ½, use a for loop to generate a random number each time through the loop and let heads be a value less than 0.50.

4.10-2. Plot the function $y = x + \sin(x)$ over the interval $0 \le x \le x_{max}$, using a while loop to determine the value of $x_{max}$, such that $y(x_{max}) = 5.7$. Notice that you cannot determine the value of $x_{max}$ explicitly.

4.10-3. Create a program that:

a. Prompts users to input a number between 1 and 10.

b. If the input is correct, prints the phrase "Your Number is X".

c. Otherwise, prints the phrase "You did not enter a number between 1 and 10".

4.10-4. Create a program that:

a. Prompts users to enter a grade from 0 to 100.

b. Prints the following message: "The Student's grade is X".

c. Using the following grade scale:

i. 90–100 is an *A*

ii. 80–89 is a *B*

iii. 70–79 is a *C*

iv. 60–69 is a *D*

v. <60 is an *F*

4.10-5. Create a program that uses the switch-case statement that:

a. Prompts users to enter an amount of US dollars.

b. Prompts users to enter the desired currency (Yen, Euros, RMB).

c. Calculates and prints the message "US$xx.xx = yy.yyy Yen/Euros/RMB" (as appropriate).

d. Use the following exchange rates:

i. $1.00 = 83.692 Yen

ii. $1.00 = 0.7559 Euros

iii. $1.00 = 6.3254 RMB (Chinese Yuan)

4.10-6. For the following program segment:

```
t=[0:pi/4:pi];
b=4.5;
x=0;
y=cos(t);
n=1;
while x~=4
   if y(n)>=0
      disp (y(n))
      n=n+1;
   else
      x=4;
      disp 'y is negative'
   end
end
```

a. What value of $x$ will cause the while loop to terminate?
b. What is the last value of $y$ displayed?
c. What is the value of $n$ when the program terminates?

# EXERCISE 4.11 FUNCTION PROGRAMMING

4.11-1. Write a function program that calculates the factorial of a number.

4.11-2. Write a function program that has multiple input and output arguments. A series RLC circuit has a resonant frequency given by the formula $f = \frac{10^6}{2\pi\sqrt{LC}}$, where $f$ is the frequency in kilohertz (kHz), $L$ is the inductance in microhenrys (μH), and $C$ is the capacitance in picofarads (pF). For these units, inductive and capacitive reactances are given by

$$X_L = \frac{2\pi * f * L}{10^3} \text{ and } X_C = \frac{10^9}{2\pi * f * C}.$$

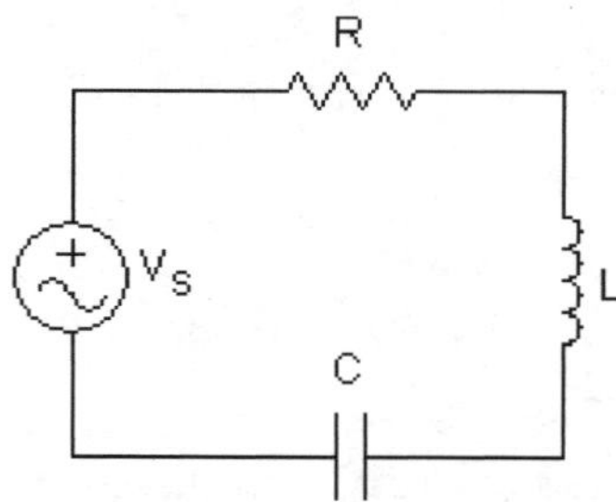


Write a function program that has the following input arguments: $L$, $C$, and $f$. The outputs are to be resonant frequency ($f$) in kHz and the inductive and capacitive reactances in ohms (Ω) for the input frequency.

Write a program that requests the values for $L$, $C$, and $f$ from users and then calls the RLC function program to output the results with labels and units. Interesting Question: What happens to the reactances as frequency varies away from resonance?

4.11-3. Write a function program to perform linear interpolation of a table of values, called interp(arg1, arg2, arg3, arg4, arg5), that has five values/variables in the argument list. Those arguments would be the (i) known value, (ii) table entry higher than the known value, (iii) table entry lower than the known value, and (iv) higher and (v) lower table entries of the unknown value to be found. The output value of the function will be the single interpolated value, calculated from the table entries.

Then, given the following table of thermodynamic properties and a specific volume ($V$) of 0.2795 $m^3$/kg, determine (using the interp() function) the temperature ($T$ in °C):

| $T$ (°C) | $V$ ($m^3$/kg) |
|---|---|
| 200 | 0.20602 |
| 250 | 0.23275 |
| 300 | 0.25799 |
| 350 | 0.28250 |
| 400 | 0.30661 |

4.11-4. Write a function program that takes as an argument any angle in radians and returns the equivalent angle that is less than $2\pi$. For example, 10 radians is equivalent to 3.72 radians. Test your function for angles = [2, 15, 45].

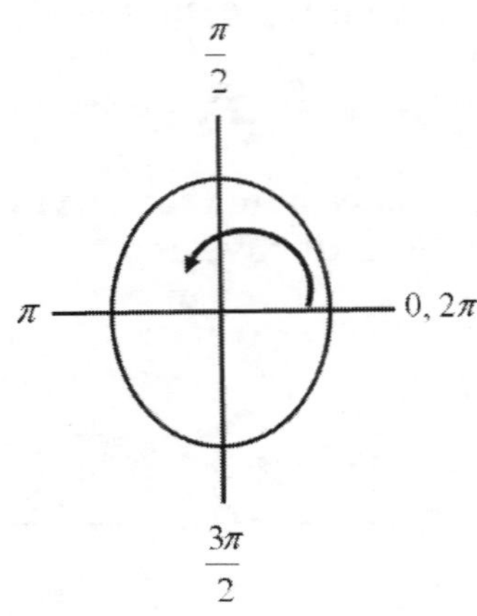


4.11-5. Given the function $y = 0.025x^5 - 0.0625x^4 - 0.333x^3 + x^2$

a. Plot the function over the range $-2 \le x \le 4$.

b. Find the $x,y$ coordinate where the function has a minimum (i.e., slope = 0) over that range, other than the trivial $x = 0$ result.

4.11-6. Write a function program called vectable that has a vector of real numbers as an input argument. The output is a 2D matrix with four rows. The number of columns will be the length of the input vector. Row 1 is the input vector. Row 2 is the square root of each element of row 1. Row 3 is the natural logarithm of each element of row 1. Row 4 is the sine of each element (assume angles in degrees) of row 1. Test your function for the following vector: vec = [33 2 9 13 3 21].

4.11-7. Define the function $g(x) = \cos(2\pi x)$. Evaluate $g(0.5)$.

4.11-8. Write the TI-89 command to create the function $\text{curl}(x) = \sin^2(x) * \ln(x)$, using the **Define** command.

# EXERCISE 4.12 MORE PROGRAMMING PRACTICE

4.12-1. Find the value of $x$ (to two decimal places) when $y$ is a minimum, using a *while* loop. Plot the function.

$$y = x^2 - 4x + 2$$

4.12-2. Write a function program that determines the properties of a cube, given the length of any side s. The properties are volume, total surface area, and length of the center diagonal (i.e., through the center of the cube). The function should work with both scalars and vectors as input arguments. Test the function.

4.12-3. Write a function program that plots a rectangle, given the $x,y$ coordinates of the center (where $c$ is a two-element vector of those coordinates), height ($h$), and width ($w$) in consistent units. Use the function to plot the following rectangles:

a. $c_x = -3, c_y = 4, h = 1.6, w = 3$

b. $c_x = 0, c_y = -5, h = 12, w = 4.5$

4.12-4. Write a function program that plots a circle, given the $x,y$ coordinates of the center (where $c$ is a two-element vector of those coordinates) and radius ($r$). Hint: Use parametric equations. Use the function to plot the following circles:

a. $c_x = 3.5, c_y = 2.0, r = 8.5$

b. $c_x = -4.0, c_y = -1.5, r = 10$

# EXERCISE 4.13 PROGRAMMING WITH LOOPS

4.13-1. Create a program that counts by 3s and outputs the results from 0 to 30.

4.13-2. Create a program that inputs 10 grades and finds the average.

4.13-3. Create a program using the for loop to calculate the first 20 terms of the equation.

$$e^x = \sum_{n-1}^{\infty} \frac{1}{n!} x^n, \text{ for } x = 2.5 \text{ (Hint: use an “accumulator” variable.)}$$

4.13-4. Create a program that inputs an unknown number of grades and finds the average.

4.13-5. Create a program using a while loop to calculate the equation to an accuracy of three decimal places, when compared to $e^{2.5}$. Also determine how many loop iterations occurred.

$$e^x = \sum_{n-1}^{\infty} \frac{1}{n!} x^n, \quad \text{for} = x = 3$$

# EXERCISE 4.14 USING PROGRAMMING TECHNIQUES TO SOLVE DETAILED OR COMPLEX PROBLEMS

4.14-1. Given the following data:

$x = 0.03, 5.94, 10.41, 16.27, 20.79, 26.52, 31.69, 37.7, 43.57$

$y = 1.13, 4.17, 7.23, 9.60, 12.14, 14.61, 17.46, 20.12, 23.82$

a. Plot the $x$–$y$ data on a graph.
b. Perform a linear regression analysis to find slope and $y$-intercept.
c. Display the best-fit line equation on the same graph as the $x$–$y$ data.

4.14-2. Given the following table of exam scores:

| Class | Sec01 | Sec02 | Sec03 |
|---|---|---|---|
| Exam 1 | 55 | 42 | 98 |
| Exam 2 | 51 | 39 | 95 |
| Exam 3 | 63 | 43 | 94 |
| Exam 4 | 58 | 45 | 90 |

a. Create a $4 \times 3$ matrix of the numerical scores.
b. What is the top score in each section?
c. What is the average score in each section?
d. What is the average score on each exam?
e. In which section and on which exam did the highest score occur?
f. In which section and on which exam did the lowest score occur?

4.14.3. Richard cooks stew every week for his club during the months shown. Using the following table, answer the questions:

Quantity purchased (# of items)

| Material | Price ($/item) | May | June | July |
|---|---|---|---|---|
| Ground beef | 10.00 | 5 | 4 | 6 |
| Tomatoes | 3.00 | 3 | 2 | 4 |
| Carrots | 4.00 | 6 | 5 | 3 |
| Potatoes | 1.50 | 3 | 5 | 4 |
| Beans | 2.00 | 2 | 4 | 3 |

a. Create a $5 \times 3$ matrix containing the amounts spent on each item for each month.
b. Calculate the total spent in May, June, and July.
c. Calculate the total spent on each food item in the 3-month period.
d. How much was spent on the most expensive food item?
e. Calculate the total spent on all food items in the 3-month period.

4.14-4. A farmer wishes to build a cylinder-shaped silo that can hold 3000 $ft^3$ of grain. The cost of the building material is $30 per square foot. What will be the height and diameter of the silo that minimizes the material cost?